Vet Fair
@ 20
7282l

PEOPLE
OF THE FOREST

The author has spent many patient years securing this brilliant collection of photographs. In his text he has tried to capture something of the stark nature of the northern woods; perhaps certain episodes will appear grimly stark, but equally with the careful camera work they have been studiously observed. The text is episodic and largely complementary to the photographs, and that explains why sometimes it appears rather abrupt; and space has not permitted a full exposition of the background to the lives of all the birds, animals, and insects.

HANS LIDMAN

PEOPLE OF THE FOREST

THE MACMILLAN COMPANY
NEW YORK

This is a translation of *Pärlugglans skog*
by Hans Lidman, published by
Lts. Förlag, Stockholm, Sweden

First published in the United States of America by
The Macmillan Company, 1963
Library of Congress Catalogue Number 63-12866

*Illustrations printed in Sweden by
Victor Petterson Bokindustri AG*

*Text printed in Great Britain by
Oliver and Boyd Ltd., Edinburgh*

Contents

Midwinter

It was Christmas Eve. All night long the owl had been keeping watch in a pine tree not far from the brushwood by Enok's cottage.

The snow lay covered with the tracks of voles and mice, radiating out from the cottage like the spokes of a wheel. Some of the tracks ended abruptly in small round holes in the snow ; others went straight to the nearest tree and worked from one root to another ; but most of them led to the pile of brushwood, where they merged and lost themselves in a confused criss-cross.

The owl saw the animals that made the tracks, but they escaped her. In the middle of the night one of them leapt quickly out from the cottage wall. Just as the owl swooped down on it, the mouse disappeared into a hole, its tail slipped through her claws as her wings brushed the ground, tracing fine lines in the snow. From time to time another mouse peeped out from a corner of the house, but it did not dare go out. It sat there, sniffed, listened, then turned back. It was a shrewd old mouse that had lived in the cottage wall for several years : but it would come out eventually, just before dawn at the latest.

A pigmy owl whistled in the wood close by, a coarse penetrating note, sounded several times in succession.

Silence returned to the wood—deep, heavy silence.

An hour before dawn a fire was lit inside the cottage. The light from it shone out through the windows and played and danced on the snow. Odd sparks whirled out into the darkness of Christmas morning, and rose half the height of the pine trees before dying out, while the fire made a roaring noise in the iron chimney.

The door opened with a creak and a flood of light filled the opening, showing Enok as he came out, bare-headed and half dressed. He slipped off a snow-covered stone and a miniature avalanche of new powdered snow slid into his unfastened boot. He coughed, thrust his

9

hands deep into his pockets, and stood listening to the silent forest which sighed gently in the cold darkness.

Suddenly a shiver ran through him; he turned quickly and started back to the house. But he bumped into something, and felt a soft feathery body and wings brushing against his cheek and neck.

" The devil take it ! " he burst out, crouching down and waving his arms wildly. An object fell down inside his open shirt against his hairy chest. Something warm and soft ; something alive. He put his hand in and grasped a half-dead mouse, which squeaked feebly and tried to bite his hand.

Throwing the mouse to the ground Enok rushed into the cottage, seized his gun, loaded it, and kicked the door open again. In the light from the fire he could see the owl rising with the mouse between its claws. He raised his gun and took aim.

But he did not fire. As the owl reached a spruce the gun was lowered and Enok smiled awkwardly. He went back inside, hung the gun on its hook again, and let the door bang shut. Luckily it wasn't one of his own tame mice ! Perhaps it was a vole ?

Up in the spruce tree the owl tore at the mouse. Then she crept in towards the trunk of the tree, ruffled her feathers, and hunched herself up, blinking slowly and sleepily. But her sleep was disturbed by the pigmy owl's morning whistle, and by the sound of clattering from inside the cottage. The smell of frying bacon and coffee wafted past her.

At daybreak the door opened again. Enok came out with his gun, and hung it on his back over a flat, empty skin rucksack. He fastened on his skis, took the track leading down towards the swamp, and disappeared among the trees.

The owl went back to sleep.

In broad daylight the harsh note of a jay down at the brushwood roused the owl. When she opened her eyes and let her gaze wander to the cottage, through the window she could see a mouse on the table. It investigated everything—the packet of sugar, the coffee cup, and the covered butter dish. At last it climbed on to the plate and nibbled the remains of meat and fat. It made fine scratches on the surface of the plate, and two black grain-like " sausages " appeared. The jay flew over and alighted on the large lump of lard on the window-sill. A great tit, which had been at the lard, moved along to some bread-crumbs in a sardine tin, and the jay pecked at the lard without swallowing. Now it peeped into the cottage, curious and nervous.

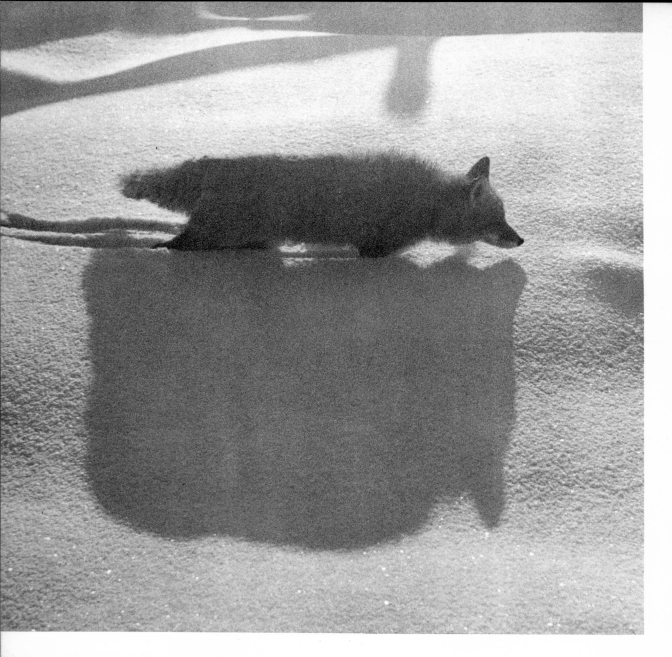

Life is hard in the winter. Animals are driven out in search of food. A weasel peeps over a snow-covered branch, a fox creeps through the snow, and a hare cowers in the thicket until night falls.

It spotted the mouse, screwed its head round even further, and let out its sharp, penetrating cry. The mouse disappeared, and it seemed to have scared itself with its own cry, for it abandoned the lard and flew up to the top of a pine tree, where it stayed alert, listening and watching. Just as the owl was dropping off to sleep again the dull echo of a shot came from up the slope of the hill.

Enok returned at midday. His fur cap was pushed to the back of his head and he had taken off his mittens, holding them round his ski sticks. There was snow on his shoulders. He moved heavily; his rucksack was bulging, and the white body of a stoat peeped out of one of the side pockets, the black tip of its tail gleaming in the sunlight. Enok took off his skis and kicked open the cottage door. Soon smoke could be seen rising vertically in the still air from the chimney, and the aroma of coffee blended with the smell of the wood smoke.

The day passed, and as twilight began to fall, Enok brought out the flayed body of the stoat and threw it on the rubbish heap. There were rustlings of life all over the rubbish heap, but nothing to be seen. Then, shrugging his shoulders, he hurried back into the warmth.

The door was barely closed before a coal tit was out pecking at the dead stoat. It took hold of a sinew, raised its tail in the air, and braced itself to pull. The owl began to get interested : she put her head on one side and blinked her large eyes. But she did not move, or even stretch. And when, in the gathering darkness, the coal tit flew into a thick bush, ruffled its feathers and settled down for the night, the owl's eyes were half-closed again. She was still satisfied and lazy from her morning meal.

Life is always like this in the forest in winter. Food is scarce, and there is a constant struggle for survival. Every bird and animal must be constantly on the watch for danger, and must spend much of its time in search of food. Only those animals who hibernate—wrapped up against the bitter cold, and skilfully concealed from prying eyes—can forget about this eternal struggle for food and security.

Moral issues do not exist in the animal world, all life is too busy with the task of mere existence.

The world is a cold, cruel, and barren place—trees and ground are swathed in a deep layer of snow—and to the casual observer there is little evidence of the life that carries on in this wilderness. Only the intricate pattern of big and small tracks in the snow, the flurry of wings in the dark, and the occasional shriek of a victim show that life has not ceased, and that the struggle goes on !

14

The death of the Golden Eagle

Not often does man invade these fastnesses in the dead of winter, but forestry work has to go on, and however cold and inhospitable the forest may be man must continue the work of felling, trimming, carting, and stacking.

So even in this wild domain there are a few men to be found—mainly foresters, and a few farmers who manage to wrest a fairly meagre livelihood from the soil. Also there is the game warden, but his territory is so vast that his task is by no means an easy one.

Squirrels are attractive little creatures, but they can also be a real pest. They are past masters of finding a way into men's houses when they are short of food, and the mess they cause can be quite chaotic. Through the work of Beatrice Potter and others we have been brought up to think of squirrels and rabbits as lovely little fluffy creatures who must on no account be harmed, but those people who have suffered from the depredations of squirrels and rabbits have rather a different outlook.

Man also is involved in this struggle for survival, so you must not be surprised if man appears from time to time in this book in the rôle of an implacable enemy to creatures which we have learned to love and protect.

So it happened that one morning, when the world lay still and silent and white, and the blanket of snow deadened even the occasional fall of a rotten branch, a shot rang out through the crisp winter air, the sound of it rebounding against the face of the hill before fading towards the slopes of the Black Hills.

Anders's little boy and his greyhound were standing under a pine tree, gazing up into the branches expectantly. Not far away Anders was pacing around holding a smoking gun.

" Did you miss ? " the boy asked.

" Not on your life," was the reply. " It is up in the tree. Give the tree a knock with your axe."

The boy hit the tree with his axe until the bark splintered off and white patches appeared on the trunk ; snow showered down from

the shaking branches like a veil. The boy jumped aside. " Keep
on hitting it ! " said his father.

Even though the boy knocked the tree until there was hardly any
snow left on the branches, no dead squirrel fell out of it.

" Cut it down," said Anders impatiently. The boy hesitated and
looked amazed at his father. " What if the keeper sees it ? " the lad
ventured. " Not much danger of that—he wont be up here for many
years, cut the pine down," Anders reassured him.

The boy chopped at the tree. The falling snow covered him :
it made its way down the neck of his shirt and melted ; it was icy
cold on his bare wrists. Eventually the pine was hewn down and

17

sank to the ground with a heavy thud. All three of them looked for the squirrel. The boy lopped the top off the tree and dragged it away, the dog sniffed and searched in the snow, but there was no trace of the squirrel anywhere.

Anders scratched his head.

Could he really have missed? Could the squirrel have leapt away in time to a neighbouring tree? He hardly believed it possible.

"We should have turned back when we saw the jay," Anders said, "they always bring bad luck." Superstition dies very hard where men live for long periods close to nature.

The dog went off on its own and in a short while its steady barking echoed through the wood. Father and son hurried in the direction of the barking, and were met by the dog creeping towards them through the snow, its tail tucked in between its legs. Above it flew a large speckled brown bird, with legs and claws outstretched, its head hanging low and its enormous wings beating. An eagle will not often attack a dog, but fear and hunger are hard masters.

Anders hardly had time to raise his gun before the dog had crept in between his legs and the bird was close above his head. The bird braked its flight and turned, brushing Anders's fur cap off his head. Anders pulled the trigger out of sheer fright; he did not have time to raise the gun high enough or to take aim; all he did was point the barrel upwards and pull the trigger.

The bird pitched, rose again and floundered away, flapping its wings heavily. Anders fired again, and scored a second hit. The bird circled, losing some feathers as it glided through the trees with wings spanned.

Anders re-loaded his gun, picked his fur cap off the ground and shook the snow off it.

"What an enormous hawk," he exclaimed, "it really is huge."

"Isn't it an eagle?" the boy asked.

"Possibly. It's all the same anyway—an eagle is a hawk and all hawks should die."

They turned and went back grouped close together, following their own tracks home. The dog, frightened, with ears drooping, kept in the middle. Not a word was spoken. A jay, sitting on a pine twig, watched them and turned its head, then gave a knowing wink.

A few hundred yards farther into the wood the golden eagle sank into the snow, its wings spanned. A shower of snow dislodged by a squirrel covered the dead bird.

18

The cottage by the marsh

The marsh was a big one—over a mile long and nearly half as wide. In the middle it was bleak and open, and flat as a pancake. Out there the blackcocks like to play and the hens creep around when the thaw sets in, inciting the cocks to bloody duels, leaving the frozen moss bespattered with stray feathers and down. But even now, in mid-winter, the playful cocks sometimes slip out into the new snow, jumping about and spanning their tail and wing feathers. Stunted and gnarled dwarf pines, with their tops flattened by the weather, encircled the cocks' playground. Nearer the edge of the wood the pines were taller and more profuse. Many of the old pines, which used to grow on the marsh, towering above the others like strange black spears, had gradually disappeared into the hearth of Enok's cottage.

But no one could ever be short of wood in this wild country, where woodland stretches in all directions as far as the eye can see, broken only here and there by the odd lake or clearing. Old trees are always falling victim to the winter gales, and the rotting trunks provide homes for countless wild creatures. Every time the wind blows a new scattering of dead or broken branches covers the ground— it is like all life, the dead making way for the new life which is always coming into being.

The cottage belonged to and was part of the marsh. It had stood on the hill not far from the blackcocks' playground for nearly fifty years. It had been rebuilt two or three times and changed owners just as often. Not many people knew about the cottage, and even fewer had ever seen it, as the path leading to it was a difficult one with many tracks leading off through the heather. No lonelier dwelling existed in the owl's wood.

Ilmari the Finn lived there for many years. He was the last Finn in the wood who could speak the old Finnish language. Ilmari was a true vagabond of the wood and would turn up in the most strange circumstances : if an elk had been poached, he was always there to receive his share of the meat, and if anyone found a fine

20

pearl in a mussel from the Black Stream, Ilmari bought it at cut price. Sometimes foxes would disappear from traps set by others, and rumour had it that the pelt could be found in Ilmari's cottage. But he was a skilful hunter himself. He shot the last bear in the wood and caught the last lynx living in the district. In his old age Ilmari found it difficult to keep going ; gout and nervous pains hindered him, preventing him from going out into the wood as was his wont any time of the day or night. Boiled grouse and elk steak disappeared from his menu, fish was becoming more difficult to catch, even the rabbits managed to evade him.

Ilmari weakened.

It was at this time that he started pilfering from the other farmers' sheds; picking the locks to cellars and larders and undoing window catches, he raided cupboards and shelves.

Down in the valley near the river there was one particular shed which Ilmari kept his eye on. Possibly this was because the ventilator on the one side was large enough to let a thin person crawl through, and in his old age Ilmari became as light and thin as a shadow. These visits to the shed were a great nuisance to the owner, not only from the economic point of view.

It was the farmer's custom to leave some provisions in the shed at the end of the summer, so that he would find food there when he visited the district in the winter, and it was more than annoying to find no trace of these supplies after tramping long weary miles over very rough country. At length this thieving got too much for the farmer. One day in late autumn he set up a large bear trap on the bench close to the inside of the ventilator. When Ilmari did not go to the village at Christmas, people wondered what had happened, for it had been his custom to stay there for a few days while making his purchases. The fur dealer waited for his usual parcel of skins and the shopkeeper had to sell the roll of twine which Ilmari had asked him to keep. The villagers wondered what had happened, for Ilmari was no longer young.

Early in the New Year the farmer went up to his shed again, as wood carting was soon to begin. It was dusk when he arrived at the shed, but he noticed at once that the ladder had been moved from the house to the shed, and up at the ventilator he could see two stiff human legs sticking out. The farmer trembled as he opened the two locks to the shed and then lit a match. In the dim light he could see Ilmari caught in the bear trap. Apparently Ilmari had crawled in through the ventilator head first, keeping his arms flat against his body, down straight into the trap. The teeth of the trap closed tightly round his neck and chest, imprisoning him there.

Fortunately for the farmer there was no law preventing him from setting whatever traps he liked behind lock and key. Nor did many people feel sorry for Ilmari, for there were many who had suffered from his thieving during the past few years.

Then Enok came, though no one seemed to know where he had come from.

Unrest

The forest was many miles deep. Seen from the slope of the Black Hill it seemed endless, as if it stretched on and on and on, to the end of the world.

Trees, trees, and yet more trees. Sometimes water could be seen gleaming far in the distance, and now and then the light brown of a wooden roof showed up among the trees ; but otherwise an uninterrupted sea of trees flowed from slope to slope towards the blue horizon.

This forest was very valuable. Some of the tallest and most beautiful pines were found here, together with spruces of unusual height. But there were also areas still undisturbed by axe and saw ; forgotten corners where stubble and brushwood among trees uprooted by the wind offered a comfortable home to owls and other birds, and many other tiny creatures. Forest flowers grew in profusion, and the cry of the eagle owl echoed from tree to tree. In summer the lower branches of the pines were spun with cobwebs, hanging like veils, and on warm days the air was filled with a monotonous buzzing and a humming and a droning of myriads of insects.

In recent years, however, general restlessness had reached even this far-flung forest. In the late autumn woodmen arrived to mark various trees, condemning them to death. Then the forest was divided into felling and transport and loading areas ; paths were improved, huts built or repaired, and one or two woodmen even set to work before Christmas. But it was only now, towards the end of January, that the upheaval had reached the owl's wood, bringing with it fear, disturbance, and unrest. There were days when the wood was filled with life—a new life pulsating in the dry old pines.

Early one morning under a cloudless blue sky Enok put the wedge in and pulled at the cross-cut saw a few times. The pine began to fall. He removed the saw and the wedge and moved a few paces away. The swish of the falling pine rose to a crescendo as it struck the ground with an almighty crack, and sent up a cloud of snow intermingled with pine needles and cones.

He felled two more trees, then went back to lop the branches. Chips of frozen wood whirled around everywhere as the whole forest was filled with sound of his wounding axe. Trees crashed to the ground and saws whistled in the morning air as they bit the wood. Here and

The wood is dense, affording cover and protection, but danger is always lying in wait. The call of the eagle owl echoes through the trees, and beasts of prey tramp through the snow. Long hairy lichens sway from the branches.

there a power-driven saw roared shrilly, and the smell of fresh wood and resin filled the air.

Horses and drivers followed the woodmen's track ; curses flowed freely and the reins cracked against the straining animals. Sometimes a horse reared, nervous and foaming at the mouth, driven half-crazy by the snow drifts and worn out with fear and fatigue. Wading up to their chests in snow the horses sometimes sank into hollows in the ground. They threw themselves forward, struggling and swimming through the snow, which melted on their bodies and froze again, giving the animals mantles of crystalline white.

Sometimes a horse grew nervous and bolted. Taking long leaps it thrust itself forward madly, surrounded by a cloud of snow. The driver then held the reins tightly, slackening them gradually, and sooner or later a tree-trunk lying across the path put a stop to the horse's escapade, and it was brought back to the main group.

The loads followed one another along small winding paths. The timber was then piled up high on to trucks, which made their way down the slopes and gathered at the frozen track crossing the swamp, their rumbling echoes filling the cold forest air. Shouting and singing mixed with the neighing of the horses and the ringing of the horse-bells.

At midday Enok paused for a meal. He made a fire to brew his coffee and grill a piece of meat. Somewhere in the distance he could hear the Siberian jay. It sounded like a whole flock of them, and then suddenly they were quite near. They settled all around Enok—some sat on the nearby tree stump, on the axe, on his rucksack ; one even tried to sit on the coffee tin which Enok had just lifted from the fire, but the bird felt the heat and flew away. Another jay attacked a sandwich which was lying on the ground close at Enok's side.

Enok sat down on a heap of pine twigs. As he stretched his legs and put a piece of meat on his knee, a jay immediately jumped up on to the upturned toe of his boot, turned its head and looked at the piece of meat before moving farther. Hopping along Enok's leg the jay stopped and looked around, glanced at Enok, and hopped on again to the meat, which it snatched with an odd little whistle, and flew off to the stump to eat it. One by one all the jays came to Enok's boot in turn, hopped along his leg, and received their piece of meat. When they had all been fed they moved on in search of the next fire and more meat.

When the jays departed Enok was joined by a coal tit, which flew on to his floppy hat, ran round the crown, looked down from the front

edge of the brim and met Enok's eye. It hopped down from the hat-brim to the pipe which he was smoking, gave a short twitter and looked around sharply. Slowly Enok reached for a piece of cheese, which he held up between his finger-tips. The tit hopped up on to his fingers, took the cheese and settled on his shoulders to eat it. Up it then fluttered back on the hat-brim, bobbed about for a minute or so, and flew off to the pines.

Not only the jays and the coal tits had grown accustomed to the new life in the wood. Sitting safely in a tree the capercailzie watched a convoy of woodmen as they passed. At the clearing where the wood was gathered and loaded the horses rested and were given food, while the yellowhammers came to collect the spilt grain. Even mice and voles found their way to the clearing, and every morning new tracks criss-crossed confusedly in the fresh snow. Down on the slope and the open bog snow buntings flew around in flocks, pecking at the horses' droppings and rising up again in front of the approaching horses, curving gracefully through the air, humming faintly in unison.

It was, however, the pigmy owl that showed the keenest interest in the new life of the forest. If Enok happened to go near it while he was felling trees it would start whistling, a long and monotonous whistle several times in succession. Sometimes it continued for an hour or more, even at midday, but more often in the morning or evening. When it was cloudy and not too cold, it moved from one tree to another, scarcely seen but easily heard. In the evenings when it was quiet out in the wood it moved over to the huts. Mice and voles also congregated round the huts as the rubbish heaps grew larger and larger. The garbage thrown out by the foresters provided sustenance for countless tiny creatures, which flourished and bred and increased enormously in numbers wherever there was human habitation. And of course all these little creatures in turn provided food for the pigmy owl.

But it was not only the food that attracted the owl to the huts ; it was drawn to people and their life. The bird was completely fascinated by the portable radio, especially when the volume was turned full on and the sound penetrated every wall of the hut, echoing deep into the wood. One mild evening when a Beethoven sonata was being broadcast the pigmy owl went quite mad. It circled the hut several times, perched on a nearby tree, and then on the wireless aerial, on the pile of firewood and on the corner of the roof, whistling the whole time. In its ecstasy it did not notice a frightened little mouse scampering out over the trampled snow, nor did it pay any

27

attention when one of the woodmen left the hut—it even nearly landed on his matted hair.

But other animals did not like the noise and were disturbed. The eagle owl moved from the district and went up towards the slopes of the Black Hill where there were plenty of dry trees and food. Foxes and rabbits moved farther away, and it was seldom that any of the larger animals were seen near the forestry huts.

The marten no longer visited the squirrel's nest, as it was now in the middle of the felling area. Now and again it revisited its old hunting grounds, and then clipped off squirrels' tails were to be found lying under the trees. The eagle owl, which had been frightened away, paid occasional visits to the area on the high cliffs where it had been breeding as far back as memory runs. He expected to reap *some* advantages from the human invasion of the wood.

It was on one of these visits that he caught Stina's old cat. Stina was the cook in the old-fashioned kitchen which had been repaired just before the onset of winter ; she was round and plump and no longer young, but then it was impossible to get a young cook for this lonely old fashioned cottage, and Stina accompanied her husband who was one of the woodmen. But she went on one condition : that her cat might go with her. It was a thin tabby cat, deaf and half-blind and nearly twenty years old.

Of course it was agreed that the cat might go with her, the main thing was that Stina could cook, sew on buttons, and mend torn trousers. Stina was happy, she earned a lot of money that winter, much more than by baking for the farmers down in the village, and her husband helped her with the heavy work of carrying wood and water. During the day she enjoyed the cat's company, giving it cream and meat and letting it out to the wood-pile in the morning and evening. On one clear moonlight night the cat seemed restless. It had been out, but wanted to go out again, twitching its tail nervously and grunting deep down in its throat. It was late, and the woodmen had gone to bed. Stiffly the cat strutted across the clearing just outside the cottage. It sat down and listened, but heard nothing, and saw nothing.

Suddenly a blood-curdling cry pierced the night, followed by a hollow rumbling in the metal chimney. All the woodmen jumped up, Stina rushed screaming to the door, followed by about a dozen men in vests and pants ; some were barefooted, others had slipped their shoes and socks on. " What was it ? What has happened ? " everyone was asking.

29

No one but Stina knew, and she continued screaming madly. Soon another sound coming from the roof could be heard above Stina's screams. Up on the roof the cat could be seen lying in the moonlight, beside the chimney. Stina's screams died down to a quiet whimper. Everyone was puzzled and a ladder was fetched from the front of the cottage. One of the woodmen put on gloves and boots and started climbing the ladder. Suddenly a vast and silent shadow passed across the roof, and an enormous bird dived down and dug its claws into the cat's body, lifting it up behind the chimney, flying out over the valley, immense in the moonlight, with the cat's gurgling death-cry echoing and then fading out.

Standing silently the men stared and listened ; no one spoke a word. Back inside the cottage they found Stina sitting crying.

" Listen Stina," one of the younger men of the team said to her, " you don't want to start crying for that old tabby, she is so old and tough that the owl can't eat her."

No one appreciated the joke, no one laughed. Thoughtfully the men crept back into their bunks and lay silently with their eyes open, thinking about the brutality of the wild world which they had come to devastate.

For the wild places of this world are cruel places, where life is lived by all creatures in a constant state of fear—fear of starvation, fear of the other wild creatures. All creatures have to fight to survive, have to fight to bring forth young, and protect them from marauders. There is no time for sentimentality, even if animals, birds, and reptiles were capable of feeling this human emotion. Once a wild creature is dead it has ceased to exist, and its mate will callously leave it in search of another mate, or in search of the next meal.

Food is all important, and if life has to be risked in search of food that is just the natural state of affairs. The ability to find food generally means the skill, the strength, and the cunning to outwit some other living creature—and this still must be applied remorselessly, again and again, as long as life lasts.

Nature in the raw is cruel—and yet not cruel, for cruelty in the human sense so often implies the intent to hurt, the joy of causing suffering for its own sake. Nature is never without purpose, and if one creature is constantly killing other creatures, that is simply because this is necessary in order to survive. We must constantly be on our guard against attributing human feelings—or human thoughts and intentions—to other forms of life.

Tracks in the snow

One morning as the gale was blowing, whirling the snow around, the driver who collected Enok's wood called to him. He had just followed the path across the mire, and said " Now they have appeared again."

" What have ? " asked Enok.

" Those big tracks, you know the ones. They crossed the path down at the bog."

Enok asked whether they were new tracks.

" Undoubtedly," was the reply. " There wasn't a flake of snow in them. By the way, the horse shied at the sight of the tracks."

A glint came into Enok's eye as he stroked his axe shaft, then he asked quickly, " Were they round or oblong ? What were they like ? "

" Oblong, and at the side of the path they were particularly big. They looked rather as though a man had jumped . . ."

Enok did not wait to hear any more. He collected his tools and hid them among the spruce branches lying around, put his axe in the sack, shouldered his rifle, and fastened his skis on. He made his way along the track down towards the bog. He knew the tracks must have been made by a wolverine, and just down there by the bog the deer liked to roam among the birch and willow or pines. He knew there was a young buck and a young doe whose mother had disappeared around Christmas when the first wolverine tracks were seen. He knew that wolverines returned every year around Christmas, coming down from the north-west. Their course went straight through the owl's wood, and year after year the large tracks would appear, leading over bog and hill. Not even the elk felt safe at this time of year, and traps would be raided and plundered day after day.

The wolverine is a rather ugly animal, about three feet long and a foot high, rather like a small and stunted bear—though it belongs rather to the weasel family. It is perhaps better known by its other name—the glutton—which it lends to common usage for describing a person with a voracious but unparticular appetite.

34

Indeed it devours an enormous amount of food for its size, and is not very fussy where its food comes from. It is entirely carnivorous, and will feed on hares, foxes, frogs, fish, mice, and other small animals —and even on deer if it can catch them. It is notorious for the annoyance it causes to trappers, by robbing their traps of both bait and captured animals.

Like the skunk, the wolverine has special glands which produce a foul-smelling fluid, and this announces its presence to its victims unless it can stalk them from well down-wind. As a result of this, it has become very skilful in concealment and stalking, and can frequently wriggle or slink up to within a few yards of a victim without being spotted ; from this final point of vantage it makes a last-minute rush or frontal assault, which leaves the victim no time to turn and flee.

To its disadvantage, its fur has some commercial value, and when its presence is known or suspected in an area it will be hunted remorselessly by farmers, foresters, and indeed all the people who live in the area. But it generally stays in its burrow in the daytime, and comes out to hunt only in the hours of dusk or darkness. For this reason, men who hunt it must be up early in the mornings, or must be prepared to pursue it into the long hours of darkness.

For its size it is a remarkably powerful animal, endowed with a rare cunning. This—combined with its valuable fur and its evil reputation as a thief—ensures that it will be hunted whenever it invades a district inhabited by man, but at the same time makes it a remarkably difficult animal to catch or kill.

Enok increased his speed, the snow flying up all around him. The wolverine had been prowling around the swamp for twenty-four hours now, and its tracks crossed the narrow strip of swamp out to the west. On the higher land to the north the animal had lain in the snow and watched. Sometimes it would see the willow bushes move, and occasionally it caught sight of a buck's head stretching for buds and twigs. Now and then the sweet scent of deer would be wafted across causing the saliva to collect in the wolverine's mouth and its empty stomach to rumble, and the animal would draw in its claws as though it had cramp. But the weather had been against the intruder : there was no wind, not a cloud in the sky, and no new snow, only a thin crusty sheet of ice which squeaked and creaked at every step.

During the daytime the deer usually went up to the clearing to eat young plants and have a rest. The plants were dense in patches,

36

but they were low on the ground, and only a stone's throw away lay the pine forest, dense and dark. The view from the edge of the forest was wide, and the risks were few.

The sky clouded over towards evening and the wind rose from the east, bringing small dry snowflakes whirling around. The wolverine sniffed at the frozen air. By dawn the wind had changed to north and brought with it a snow storm. The edge of the wood braved the full force of the wind, and the birch and willow offered poor shelter. By midday the deer had had enough of their draughty feeding place and made their way up to the clearing, hoping to find a quieter and more sheltered spot.

The wolverine watched them. Pressing itself down on the ground it retreated into the wood, and circled round. It crossed the main track and crept up towards the clearing until it reached the far side. Through the falling snow it could see the deer going among the plants, nibbling them and sinking up to their chests in the snow so that only their heads were visible. Sheltering among the thicker and higher plants, it crept and slid forward, tensing its claws and letting its chest sink into the snow. Any sound was absorbed by the soft blanket of snow, and the headwind removed any scent.

Enok found the tracks in the middle of the swamp, but by now the new snow had covered some of them and they did not lead down to the bog, but up to the clearing, straight into the wind. He increased his speed. He remembered the fox that had been caught in the trap between Christmas and New Year, and by the time he came to look at his trap the fox had been clipped in half, as though cut by an enormous pair of scissors, and half of it was missing. He also thought of the wood grouse he had hung in a pine tree on New Year's Eve while he followed a new mink track. He did not catch the mink, and when he returned to fetch the grouse it was gone. Only a maze of tracks under the tree told the tale.

Last winter the wolverine had had a narrow escape. Enok had spotted the tracks down by the lake and had followed them down along the swamp and up the far slope. On the far side of the hill it seemed as though the beast had suddenly changed its course and started to creep, resting a while behind a tree stump before leaping up on to the neck of a stray elk cow. It had bitten really hard and the cow had jumped up showering snow all around, and made away in long bounds. Blood and tufts of fur bespattered the ground.

Last year there had been a heavy fall of snow bending many of the

38

The mink is a newcomer to the wood. It really prefers the streams and rivers where it can catch fish, but during the winter it leads a secluded life hidden in holes or among stones. Now and again it creeps up into the snow, and on these occasions neither the squirrels nor the birds are safe from its powerful jaws.

young birch trees under the weight. The elk rushed under a bent birch tree, the stem brushing along its neck and back, so that the wolverine received a whack and was torn off the elk and thrown into the snow. There it lay for a while completely stunned while the snow thawed under its body. After that the large tracks continued due north and were seen no more that winter. The elk recovered and its wound healed, and the wolverine had gone hungry for a while longer.

When Enok reached the taller pines he noticed that the tracks changed to a kind of furrow, as though the wolverine had crept along on its stomach. Winding and twisting, the furrow stopped near two bushes which lay close together, the snow was well-trodden and there were clear prints of the pads of the hind paws and claw scratches. The wolverine had lain in wait among the pines, hunched together with its hind paws dug into the snow ready to jump. Between the branches it could see the deer plucking the pine shoots, keeping close together to shelter one another from the cold and the wind. Nearer and nearer, step by step, a buck approached the lurking wolverine. A sudden gust of wind snapped a twig with a crisp clear crack, and enveloped the buck in a swirling cloud of snow.

In two long leaps the wolverine reached the buck, and as it turned its head it felt the wolverine's teeth in its neck. Rearing up the buck spun round, spluttering and coughing. Doubling its efforts it rushed towards the wood with the wolverine clinging to its throat. Before long, however, the buck stumbled over a fallen tree and collapsed in the snow.

In vain the buck tried to rise, but the wolverine bit its head right off, tearing some meat from the neck which it ate greedily. It then took the head between its claws and carried it off into the wood. After selecting one of the larger pines it climbed nimbly up, wedged the head firmly between two sturdy branches, and returned to the deer's body. Tearing open the breast it filled its hungry stomach with warm steaming meat. This was indeed a repulsive meal, made by an animal repulsive in appearance and of repulsive habits.

When Enok reached the spot where the wolverine had lain in wait he took his gun, loaded it and pressed it under his right arm ready to fire. Taking a few steps forward he stopped and listened, and after another two paces he saw the buck's tracks. Just then he noticed something moving behind a bush, and a hairy body with short legs and bushy tail could be seen making for the wood. Enok raised his gun, but it was difficult to take aim as the whirling snow was in his eyes and the wolverine moved quickly. Just before the fluffy mass disappeared, however, a shot echoed dully before it was smothered by the snow. The wolverine gave another leap and disappeared behind a bush, rolling like a soft ball. Holding his ski sticks ready to strike Enok rushed forward.

But there was no wolverine, not even a drop of blood, only a few hairs lying on the snow. Another inch and the beast would have been his.

Throwing his gun over his shoulder Enok set off on his skis, following the track straight into the wood. Down at the edge of the wood he could see the beast bounding through the snow irregularly, but it was getting more difficult to follow it through the blinding snow. Just as he took aim, the wolverine stopped and looked back. He fired, but his shot went wide. The chase continued. The lead was reduced now, but the target was still moving quickly, and just as he reloaded the black ball of fur disappeared into the wood. He was furious, flung off his waistcoat and sweater, and continued the chase in his shirt sleeves, covered in sweat, spurred on by the intense excitement of the hunt.

Time went by, and now and then he saw twigs moving after the wolverine had knocked against them, and from time to time he spotted a black fluffy mass creeping for shelter. Increasing his speed he tried to head the wolverine off. Mile upon mile the tracks led to the north-west, over steep hills and through virgin snow, but never over swamp or moor where the snow lay too soft and deep.

Towards evening Enok had an attack of cramp and gave up the chase. He did not dare to continue, as the district was strange to him and he did not know if there were any huts or shelters. Lighting a fire to boil some coffee, he ate his sandwiches, rested a while, and turned to go back. The blizzard continued, but now he was going with the wind. As darkness fell he lost his tracks, and continuing more by instinct he made his way to the swamp and the open wood, from where he could see the hills like black shadows in the snow.

An oppressive silence lay over the forest as Enok moved wearily homewards, tired and disappointed. Not a sound was to be heard, except the gentle swish of his skis as they ploughed a track through the deep soft snow.

From time to time a branch would release its load of snow and spring skywards, while the snow thudded dully on the white blanket

41

below. If Enok chanced to snap a twig with his skis, the sound would be dulled and almost lost in the great white world.

The whiteness was almost terrifying in the half light, even to Enok, who had spent so much of his life in the forest. It was quite difficult to tell where land ended and sky began, and only the trees served to give some sort of perspective to the unchanging scene. But the sheer monotony of the scene oppressed him as much as the stillness, and at times he could hardly resist the impression that he was standing still, while countless trees swept silently and inexorably past him.

During the night the storm eased, the sky cleared, and the moon shone down from between the fleeting clouds. The cold set in, and the surface of the snow acquired a frozen crust. Enok's arms and legs were numb with cold and he was well nigh exhausted, but he did not dare to rest, not even to pause for a moment.

By midnight he reached the swamp and could hear foxes barking from the pine where the dead buck lay. No doubt they were feasting on it, and he felt he ought to go over and fetch the body away as there was still a lot of meat on it, but he was too tired. It was as much as he could do to drag himself to the cottage ; to food and warmth and dry clothes.

Only those who have ploughed through deep snow till they have reached a state of almost complete exhaustion can know the feeling of sheer joy which comes over them when at last they can collapse on a bed, put the legs up and allow the blood to flow back out of the feet, and feel the tired muscles relax. For hours on end they have battled against exhaustion, forcing the unwilling limbs to keep moving in an almost mechanical manner, and now at last they can turn off the machine, and enjoy the almost unbelievable luxury of complete relaxation.

The following day was clear and sparkling. The new snow was dazzling white, soft and billowy between the trees and ruffled by the wind in the open spaces. By the time Enok reached the battlefield, the snow there was covered with all kinds of tracks. The jays and tits had left, and high overhead black ravens circled round.

The roe buck lay in the trampled snow, almost completely devoured, but no bird nor animal had found the head up in the tree, safely lodged between the branches, its black eyes staring sadly into the bitter cold.

March

The weather held for a whole week after the snow storm. The air seemed to creak with cold, and at night stiff frozen birds would from time to time fall lifeless into the snow.

Night after night throughout the winter, countless small birds would fall to the ground in this way, overcome by cold, exhaustion, or starvation—or a combination of all three. This was the hard time of year for all living creatures, but the owls were glad of this harvest of little birds lying around the roots of the trees. Food of any sort was hard to come by, and they could not afford to be fussy because their more accustomed fare of mice, voles, and other small animals was simply not on the menu.

The blackcocks could withstand the cold better. These shrewd calculating birds buried themselves in the snow during the keenest frost, down in their snow holes they would ruffle up their feathers and remain quite still, keeping themselves warm with their own heat. However, sometimes by the late forenoon the longing for a birch bud was often too strong, and digging themselves out they would go on their way. Sitting and swinging up and down on the outer branches of a birch, the cocks looked like shiny black balls, stretching their necks after buds to satisfy their craving. They stuck out their heads, pulling them in again quickly whenever a sudden gust of wind hit them. Perhaps the cocks felt the warmth of the spring sun, perhaps not. At the first sign of approaching dusk they would creep back into their holes out on the clearing, where the fox seldom passed and where the hawk could not surprise them.

For the fox suffered perhaps more from hunger than most creatures during the winter, and competed with the birds of prey for the few small animals and birds which were to be found. His fine russet coat was shabby and faded, his ribs showed through, and his brush trailed disconsolately on the snow.

All wild life was driven away by the intense cold. The squirrel, usually so bright and cheery, remained cold and uncertain in its nest. However, at the first sign of the sun it jumped out. Shivering with cold it ran up the pine, leaping from one branch to another, chattering

Down by the swamp the field vole is the commonest rodent, but is seldom seen as it spends most of its time hidden in the grass and snow. But one day the snow covering cracks and a little black nose pushes its way through, followed by two shining eyes.

It digs itself out, round and clumsy, with its short tail dragging, it scuttles over the snow looking rather like a ball. It pauses to have a look at some dead flowers, hoping to find some seeds.

away impatiently until it found a cone-covered tree in the sun. It stayed up there for hours on end, breaking the cones and rustling the pine needles slightly. Suddenly the shadow of the old goshawk appeared above the trees, its eyes searching for food.

By now the squirrel had had enough to eat and darted in amongst the thicker branches, staying there for a while shivering with cold and fear. As it crept out it looked around cautiously before leaping over to the next tree, stopping to listen now and again on its way back to its nest. Just as it was about to jump into its nest the hawk hurtled down like a grey ball, catching the tip of the squirrel's tail and nearly sweeping it off the branch with its wings. The animal clung desperately to the branches, swayed and threw itself in towards the tree trunk, and dropped down into its nest, shaking the whole tree. It filled up the entrance to its nest with moss and twigs, and sank down exhausted, its tiny heart pounding.

The shrew had been curled up in a warm hole in the earth when it was wakened by the March sunshine. Driven by uncontrollable curiosity, it had left the warmth of earth and snow and climbed up along a root, losing its way in the driven snow. It jumped around and sniffed, blinded by the strong sun, floundered in the snow. Scuttling round in small circles it turned nervously until it knocked against a high projecting ridge of snow. It followed the ridge, getting further and further away from its root. A shiver ran down the grey-blue fur, its small black eyes closed. This was the shrew's greatest adventure, and it would never live to tell the tale. Within an hour the tiny animal was exhausted, and a small grey-black frozen ball of fur remained curled up in the snow, asleep for ever in the cruel cold.

The vole also was unable to control itself, and driven by its curiosity it slowly dug its way out through the new snow at the edge of the bog where the withered maiden grass grew. The stems were buried in snow and only the shrivelled tops could be seen. Suddenly the surface of the snow cracked and a black nose appeared, followed by two shiny black eyes. Black and soft as velvet, the vole slowly crept out of the snow, sniffing and listening, tensing its whiskers before plunging forward at a dead flower, stretching up to it in the hope of finding a few dried seeds. Sitting on its haunches, it peeled and ate them like a squirrel. Suddenly the raven's cry echoed from the hill where the dead elk lay—a harsh and angry sound. In two quick hops the vole was back in its hole, sliding down quickly and softly its tail lashing like a miniature whip.

48

The otter lives down by the stream, where it fishes and whistles in the late winter nights. It loves to play in the snow, leaping forwards and backwards betweeen the young trees, and sending the snow flying.

Sometimes the otter burrows down
into the snow, tunnelling along
under the surface for a remarkably
long way, until it peeps out again,
playful and mischievous.

By midday the intense cold seemed to have eased a little, but a gentle north wind rose, whirling up small clouds of snow on the far side of the bog where the frost was keenest.

Everything was seeking shelter. The crossbill hen sat on her eggs sheltered by pine branches, while her mate flew around in search of food. The bullfinch seemed to puff itself out more than usual, and in the alder shrubs the long-tailed tits hung upside down, eagerly looking for grubs, their long tails tracing circles in the mist. The snow buntings were the only creatures that defied the cold on the swamp. Swinging to and fro together they uttered their long, plaintive song, which to-day seemed more festive than usual. The river was usually icebound for most of the late winter, the open furrow of swiftly flowing water freezing over, only leaving small round openings which steamed slightly with cold. The dipper disappeared during the storm, and the mink had crept under the ice. Only the otter appeared between the holes in the ice.

On clear nights the otters would sit eating freshly caught salmon, uttering a shrill whistle now and again as an indication of the approaching spring. Every morning the fox took a stroll and passed the otters' feeding place before the ravens and jays got there, as there was always plenty of fish to be found. It was on such icy cold days when the wind was blowing down the narrow valley that the otters would feel playful. Rushing through the deep snow on the river banks they would chase one another playfully, summersaulting and jumping around in wild play, hidden in a cloud of snow. Diving into the snow they would burrow down, and now and then a little black head would pop up looking for its playmates. Their lively game would continue for some time before they went back through one of the holes in the ice, and the cold driving mist enveloped the river bank.

Up among the alders the hazel hen also seemed to feel the approach of spring. An old elk had been roaming around the alders since Christmas, now and then investigating the neighbouring land, but on this cold day it went off for a stroll, perhaps in order to keep itself warm. Stepping nimbly the animal made its way through the alders the snow often reaching to the tops of its legs. The hazel hen got excited. Ruffling its feathers it moved along the pine branch it was sitting on and started singing a fine lilting song, rising at the end. The elk listened, putting its large ears forward and opening its nostrils to sniff. It moved forward a little and saw the bird. Forgetting the cold and the snow, the hazel hen hopped around, ruffling itself up,

53

singing song after song. The elk raised its head and listened, blinking its large eyes, its mouth gaping and its breath rising like puffs of steam.

Standing there the two creatures seemed to amuse each other—the small soft feathery hazel hen and the large clumsy elk—while the sun sank slowly and another icy cold night gripped the owl's wood. And so life goes on in the forest, as March brings the first faint promise of spring. There are more hours of sunshine each day, and as the warmth pours down on to the snow-laden branches of the pines, the dull plop, plop, plop can be heard of snow dropping off the branches into the soft blanket of deep snow which covers the ground. Sometimes the warm sun comes suddenly after a heavy snowfall, and then this thudding of snow falling from the branches can be oddly continuous, yet uneven. Branches eased of their load spring up towards the sky, scattering a fine powder spray.

Gradually the snow dwindles, the ice melts from the lakes and ponds in the forest, and the rustlings of life become more widespread and more numerous. Wild creatures cannot of course remember what the previous spring was like, but instinct tells them that change is in the air, that food will be easier to find, and that life will consist of rather more than a bare existence. There is a strange magic in the air, and all life falls under its spell.

But spring is not yet here, and snow lingers on in drifts and patches in the forest—some of them small, some covering wide areas on north facing slopes where the sun only shines obliquely, or where the snow is sheltered by trees from the dissolving warmth. At this time of year the impacted frozen snow can sometimes look almost unbelievably beautiful, gouged and moulded by the wind into long wavy ridges and troughs.

This is a very different snow from the light, ethereal, powdery substance which lay on the branches and covered the roofs of the foresters' huts. This is hard, firm, and solid—thawed and refrozen time and time again, until it has formed a solid mass which will take days and weeks of warm spring sunshine to clear it from the ground.

These drifts of frozen weather-worn snow take on the reflections of the light and colour around them. On a grey day they are dull and featureless and uninteresting, but in a flaming red dawn they sparkle with the deep blues, reds, and yellows of the sky. No longer are they formless and lifeless masses of white or grey, but scintillating pools of living and quivering light and colour.

56

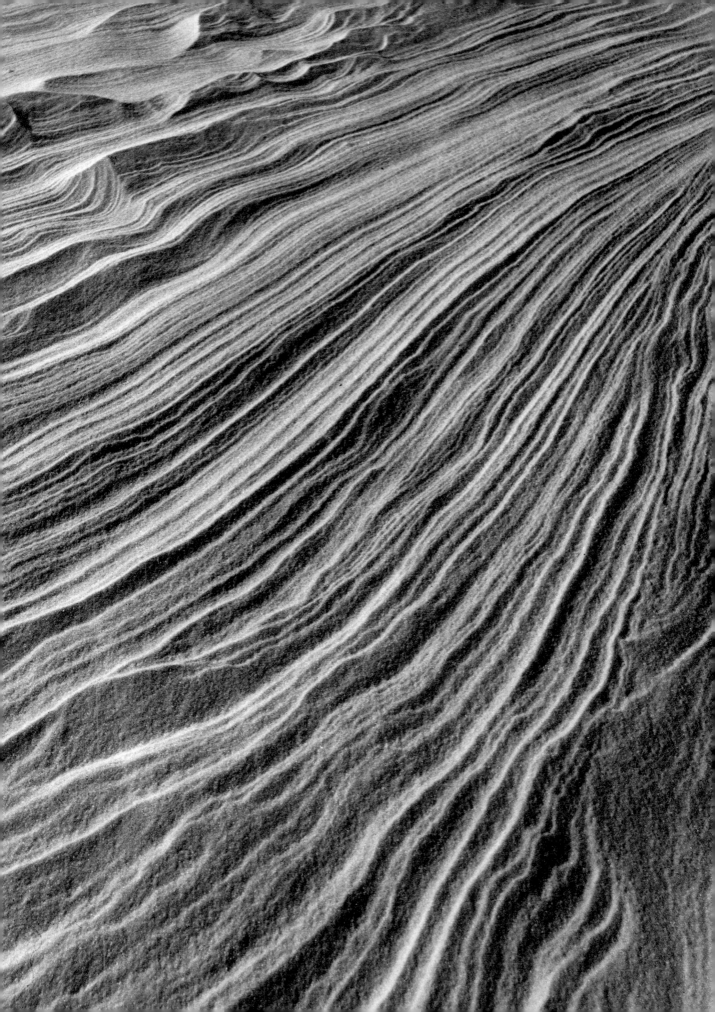

A sign of spring

The winter lost its grip after the cold spell in March. The weather changed, the wind veered to the south, and by the beginning of April the thaw had really set in. Trees became uncovered and the patches of snow dwindled ; the air was mild and still, filled with the smell of resin and sap.

On such mornings the owl sat in a pine tree near the slope where the capercailzie liked to court. Digging her claws well into a dry branch, the owl would let her gaze wander in search of a vole. The air was misty and silent. Unnoticed, daybreak crept in among the pines and as the mist lifted, bark and lichens covered with poisonous looking yellow berries came to view. In the increasing light the covering of snow seemed to widen, lying over the earth like a white blanket.

But it was a wet blanket, this mantle of snow which still lay heavily on the earth in patches, and was receding rapidly. Every day the patches of snow grew smaller, and as soon as the snow revealed the bare earth, little groups and clusters of flowers would spring up, heralding the arrival of a new year, and the birth of new life.

The icicles had melted from the edge of the streams, and once again their waters flowed swift and clear through the forest, gurgling and chattering over the boulders.

It was too early yet for there to be many frogs about, but as the ice melted from river and pond and lake, innumerable little creatures came back to life from their long spell of hibernating. Countless millions of lives had been lost in the frozen waters during the long winter, but more had survived, and soon the waters would be teeming with life once more.

At the first sign of dawn the silence was broken by faint clicking sounds, repeated and becoming more distinct and quicker, ending in an explosive sucking noise, rather like a cork coming out of a bottle. This call was repeated several times, and then new clicking sounds could be heard from the far side. A large bird glided over, stopping suddenly and falling into the snow, almost knocking against the owl. For a moment the cock capercailzie stood there with neck outstretched, looking and listening, as though amazed at its own boldness. After

58

The marten is one of the roaming visitors to the wood, seldom having a steady abode. But should it find an area rich in food, it will stay there a while. Taking an empty woodpecker's hole to sleep in, it will return there after hunting, and sit in the hole to keep a look-out and see whether anything is happening nearby. Should it be thirsty it can always go down to the snow.

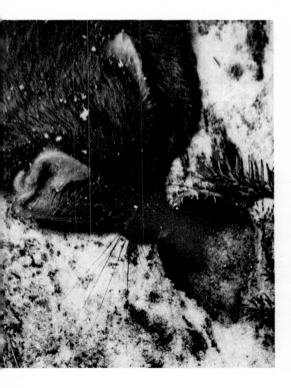

taking a few paces, it ruffled up its neck feathers, fanned its tail feathers out broadly, and pointed its beak to the sky. It gave a cautious display. Rushing down from the other side, another cock appeared, landing about a stone's throw from the owl. Filled with energy and excitement the first cock repeated its display again and again, neck outstretched, wings flapping, prancing around with its beak open, walking stiff-legged, almost stumbling—but he was not blind. The second cock hopped in towards it, prancing around.

The cocks were only a few feet away from each other, more or less equal in size, and both puffed out and gripped by the excitement of their dance. The owl began to show interest and turned her head, blinking her huge eyes. These large birds were disturbing her, in fact almost frightening her, and she was not quite sure what to do. She drew herself up, making herself long and thin, stiffening and letting her gaze wander out beyond the cocks to the pine tree on the far side. Over there she could see a dark brown oval animal creeping out of the tree trunk. It was the marten that lived in the Black Hills, the one with the dirty yellow patch on its throat. Creeping along cautiously the marten took cover behind the tree trunks and bumps in the snow. Hiding behind a tree trunk it sat and waited while the cocks pranced around in wild ecstasy. The cocks infuriated one another more and more. Jumping around they dragged their wings in the snow, their tails fanned out. Dancing round each other they came closer and closer to one another but did not touch each other—it was still too early for the hen to come.

The light increased, and it was soon as light as it would ever be on such a misty April morning. The owl moved in towards the trunk of the tree, stretched her legs, making them look like thin sticks. She seemed to look different, almost unrecognisable, as she stared and stared at the marten, hardly blinking.

Prancing around, one of the cocks drew near the tree where the marten was hiding. The cock danced, jumping around with wings relaxed, neck bent almost backwards, insensible to all danger. Darting out, the marten left a wide dark track in the snow. It bit the cock's neck, tearing with its claws and sucking like a leech. The stiff stare vanished from the cock's eyes, its expression became frightened as it beat its wings more furiously, whisking the snow into the air, and rushed off towards the pines of the swamp.

The other cock could not understand what had happened, but became alarmed at its mate's hasty flight and also disappeared.

60

For a long time the owl remained sitting pressed against the tree trunk, but at last she relaxed and was as round as a ball again.

Of all the woodsmen, Anders was probably the earliest to be out and about in the mornings. He regarded it as a matter of pride to be first in the wood, and those mornings when he had managed to get his load and drive down the track, meeting his mates on their way up, he would give a satisfied grin. However, early rising made him tired and irritable.

And so it was that one April morning he sat on his sledge in a doze, grumpy, sleepy, and cold. Now and then he started up, called to the horse, giving the reins a tug and then sinking back again. Out on the swamp he was awakened by the crowing of the cocks. Far out the swamp was black with a seething mass of birds; the air seemed to quiver, pierced now and again by a cackling kro-ko-ko-karr as the cocks flew at each other, causing feathers and down to sweep out over the snow.

Anders rubbed his eyes. As he straightened his fur cap a capercailzie cock flew out straight towards him. There seemed to be something wrong with the bird, it appeared to be unnaturally fat around the neck and breast and flew in a most peculiar fashion, beating its wings as though it were trying to rise vertically from the ground. Stopping his horse, Anders stood up. Just then the cock's wings folded up and the bird hurtled down like an unshapely feathery ball. Dancing on the snow in the path just in front of the horse, it bounced back and lay still in the middle of the track. A marten crept out from among the feathers. After a few shaky steps along the track it stopped, arched its back and vomited. Staring at Anders with its back arched it licked its lips, then hopped on to the snow at the side of the track and slunk off towards the wood, moving unsteadily until it was lost among the dwarf pines on the edge of the swamp.

Lifeless the cock lay in the middle of the track. Anders went down to it, lifted its head and saw a row of tooth marks. Lower down the neck he found a long open cut. It was an old bird, and quite a large one. Anders took a cautious look around, stuffed the bird into his hay-bag and whipped his horse on, whistling to himself. Now he was awake—really awake.

After loading his wood Anders made up a fire, ate his sandwiches, and drank his coffee, resting a while to let his horse cool down. Siberian jays appeared and joined him, though he did not know where they had come from. They sat on his rucksack and hopped round the fire, whistling very faintly and wailing at irregular intervals. Three of

them were more than obstinate, whilst the rest of the flock were already busy building their nests.

Anders grew impatient with them. He knew that Siberian jays were a sign of bad luck—his father had told him that. He tried to chase them away, shouted and waved his arms at them, but the birds remained, looking at him amazed, begging for food. One of them tried to steal a whole packet of sandwiches, but only managed to tear the paper.

Anders grew more and more annoyed. He looked around for something to throw at the birds, but as he couldn't find anything he took out one of his knives. Aiming at one of the birds that was sitting on a low birch stump, he threw it. The knife skimmed past the bird's head and plunged into the snow, disappearing completely. Crouching down, the jays beat their wings and turned their heads. One bird hopped over to a bent alder branch and watched Anders from there. He was furious. Pulling out his other knife he threw it without taking aim—and missed. The jay stayed on the branch, amazed and puzzled. It stretched itself, ruffling its neckfeathers, but when the axe whizzed past and hit its tail, it moved away.

At last as more and more objects were hurled at them, the birds flew away. From their perch in the trees they looked on in surprise while Anders rushed around looking for his axe and knives. They saw him kicking the snow, heard him swearing, and finally he climbed on to his load and made his way down the slope.

The thaw of the last few days had loosened the mud on the track, and made it slippery and treacherous. In his excitement Anders forgot all about this and urged his horse on, lashing with the reins instead of holding them in, and at a bend half way down the long slope the front of the sledge slid over to the outside of the track, the runners dug in and the load lost its balance and toppled into the snow. Even though nothing was damaged, Anders was furious. The horse had not been pulled over, nor had his sledge been broken, but the wood had to be reloaded. At least an hour was wasted, and his advantage over the others was lost—apart from the fact that it was extremely hard work. Anders got busy with the straps and chains, unfastening them and then letting the wood slide off. He managed to set the sledge upright on the track again, unharness the horse and move it over a few paces before giving it its hay-bag.

While Anders was reloading his wood the foreman came along on skis. He stopped and watched the horse biting down to the bottom of its bag and then shake its head so that the hay flew out. With the

63

hay a large capercailzie cock fell out of the bag, with large visible wounds on its neck and breast. When Anders looked up, the foreman stood there pointing down at the cock with his ski stick. Anders tried to explain that a marten had killed the bird, but the foreman didn't say a word, only his mouth twitched nervously.

"You can see the marten's tracks down there," Anders called, "they will still be there."

The foreman said nothing, but his smile conveyed a lot. He looked almost evil as he skied past Anders down the track to the other woodmen. Anders was furious. He cursed the jays, the foreman, and his own bad luck. This would mean that he would have more trouble with the foreman, the keeper, and perhaps even with the manager. He got his load ready in record time and was soon making his way down to the swamp.

By afternoon he was the only driver who had brought down three large loads. As the others watched him enviously he forgot his bad luck with the fallen load and the cock. After all, the foreman had no witness, so it did not really matter. Sitting lazily on his sledge while his horse made its way to the cottage, Anders was tired and his head was heavy. He saw the brown alder catkins hanging on either side of the track, he heard the constantly repeated spring song of the great tits echoing down from the birches. He felt the spring air, strong and heavy, almost paralysing.

As he drew nearer to the cottage, he was roused by the barking of dogs. Sitting up and listening, he realised it was Bjorn, his greyhound. Bjorn was used for hunting elks and hares as well as anything else in the wood, so Anders listened with increasing interest. What could he have found now, he wondered? Perhaps it was the fox that had visited him during the last few nights? Or a hare down by the bog, the one which was being protected?

The barking grew louder and Anders stopped the horse at the gate to the field. Suddenly a doe ran down the track and jumped out into the snow and over the fence just near the horses. It then jumped back on to the track. Anders grew excited—venison was not an every-day meal. He drove the horse home at a gallop, grabbed his capercailzie and rushed into the house. Throwing the bird down on the floor, he went to the hearth and poured himself a cup of lukewarm coffee, which he gulped down still standing. Sitting at the window, his wife and son gazed puzzled at the empty knife holders. Anders understood their looks, muttered to himself, and finished his drink.

66

"The cocks have started; I have just caught one," he said, before reaching for his gun and collecting several cartridges from the desk drawer. As he left the house he asked his son to see to the horse.

The doe's track was unsteady and the snow soft and deep. She seemed to have changed tracks several times to lead the dog astray. Anders was too excited, changing his mind continually, jumping from one track to another, sinking into the deep snow, quivering and shaking with exhaustion. Once only did he see the doe as it leapt over a stream in the forest, but he did not fire—he did not even have time to raise his gun before it was gone.

At dusk Anders gave up the chase and put the dog on the leash. The baying stopped, but an odd hooting continued like an echo, more hastily—quick and short with repeated monotony. This time it was the owl, who was still sitting up in the pine. She continued calling for hours on end, while the darkness increased and life in the wood slowly changed its guise.

Darkness settled over the forest, creatures of the daylight retreated into hiding in hole and hollow, tree and bush, while creatures of the night came forth to prowl abroad on wing or paw, softly, warily, ever searching, listening, watching. Eternal vigilance was the price of survival, for it was necessary both to eat and to avoid being eaten.

Birds were beginning to arrive from the south. As the days grew longer and the weather warmer they would come in their hordes. But not all of them survived the long journey, and many were caught by unsuspected cold or the last of the winter storms. For winter was loth to loose its grim hold on this northern forest, and even after the signs of spring were well advanced there was always liable to be a freak frost or a sudden heavy snowfall, accompanied by gales, to threaten the new life that had come to the woods.

On still soft nights, however, the beat of wings and the strident call of geese could be heard overhead, and if there were a clear sky and a full moon there were some superb sights to be seen, as these voyagers winged their way northwards in perfect V formation, with a few stragglers trailing along in the rear.

Winter was merging into spring, snow changed to sleet and finally to gentle rain, the buds on the birches burst into leaf, odd clusters of flowers spread until they formed a carpet on the forest floor. From boulder and hollow tree, pond and stream, thicket and burrow, small creatures crept forth into this wonderful bright new world. Life was coming back to the forest.

With the first sign of spring, and the gradual emergence of life into the forest, the pairing off of the sexes began once more. We have already seen the display of the capercailzies, but the squirrels also were mating, and many of the smaller birds were appearing in brighter plumage, and singing more tunefully.

Before long the young of countless birds and animals would appear on the scene, and then the need for vigilance would be greater than ever. Many a baby squirrel would provide a tasty morsel for a marauding marten, many a baby rabbit or hare would be devoured by prowling stoat or weasel, many a baby mouse or vole would fall victim to the rapacious talons of the owls of the forest.

The wastage of nature in the raw seems appalling when we attempt to compare it with human mortality rates, but nature is nearly always well balanced, and anything which upsets that balance will have very widespread ramifications. When we observe the enormous number of embryo tadpoles in the spawn produced by a single female frog, we realise that nature makes due allowance for this enormous wastage. If countless tadpoles did not perish before ever becoming frogs, and if countless more tiny frogs were not devoured by birds within hours of leaving the water for the first time, the world would very soon be overrun by frogs.

The trees of the forest also were bursting into new life. The pines and larches were showing new points of gold or bright green on the tips of each branch, the birches were showing a delicate tinsel of new green where shortly before had been only the bare skeletons of the trees in their winter garb.

The sound of the woodmen's axes could be heard reverberating through the forest as the work of thinning went on, leaving room for the stronger trees to put on girth and grow to greater heights. For in trees also the fittest must survive, and if the hand of man speeds up the destruction of the unfit, that is merely to facilitate the growth of the surviving trees.

Even the foresters' horses seemed to sense that this was a time of rapid change, and that something unusual was in the air ; for they worked with a renewed zeal, snuffling noisily at the smell of spring. It was impossible to be in the forest at this time without experiencing this tremendous feeling of latent life—the throbbing and pounding heart of a great forest, coming to life once more after a prolonged period of enforced idleness.

Old Kare's garden

Rain, sun, and wind all speeded up the thaw. For about a week the streams were full and rushed gurgling to the swamp, turning it into an impassable bog. The ice melted on the lake and in the distance a river could be heard thundering and foaming over the rocks, swollen to several times its normal volume of water.

The snow blanket shrank and gradually disappeared. It had already gone from the clearing and the south slopes by the end of April, and the earth turned grey, brown, and black as it dried out, dry as a bone. On the warm south banks liverwort buds appeared, and the moss near Old Kare's garden turned to a soft mauvish tint. Down there the flowers crowded one another out, while dark green leaves covered the dry twigs and old leaves.

The alder, birch, and aspen came to life again, and down in the glade along the damp banks of the stream appeared thick clusters of violet-red flowers hanging from leafless stems.

This stream never freezes nor does it dry up, for it has its source from a large deep spring. The water from the spring is warm, and in January a fine mist hangs over it while the surrounding bushes are covered with large glistening crystals. Minnows dart about in the clear water, and just before mating season their bellies turn red, orange, and silver.

It was quite surprising how much life was suddenly to be seen in the forest—in the trees and bushes, in the tussocks of grass and in holes in the ground, in pools and streams, amongst the tangled roots of fallen trees, and in the moulding beds of last season's decaying leaves. Everywhere there was a rustling and a chattering, a fluttering and a calling, a sniffing of ardent nostrils at the fresh spring air with its promise of warm days to come.

The cock chaffinch arrived a week ago ; he was already hoarse from singing while waiting for his mate to help him to build a nest. The bullfinch sat in the alder, shaking its tail and letting out a long wailing whistle. The blackbird hid in the thicket, its yellow beak and

shiny black feathers just visible, its deep alto voice and clear whistle drowning all the other song birds. Not far off could be heard the deep throaty call of a pheasant, and a few minutes later a hen pheasant swept by, followed closely by the cock, their long tails trailing behind them.

Close to the foot of the maple tree the hazel hen was having a sand bath in the warm earth, opening and closing its beak, its eyes half closed in enjoyment. Up in the pines the great grey shrike had arrived, still tired and lazy after its morning meal, glancing around at the tits as though selecting its supper. In the early spring the shrike enjoyed a tit or a wren.

The battle for food and survival does not cease simply because the weather is becoming warmer. All creatures have to eat to live, and a great many of the people of the forest must eat meat—must kill and kill again, in order to survive.

Something was moving in the greyish-brown moss, heather twigs quivered and bilberry shrubs parted as a blue-grey grass snake glided out on to the stone, looking just like a dark dry twig. It paused to enjoy the warmth of the sun, opening its scales so that the yellowish-white patches on the sides of its head showed up clearly against its dull grey surroundings. Two shining bluebottles buzzed by, flying round the snake. One of them ventured to settle on the snake, but was shaken off; the other selected a twig in front of the snake where it settled down to its daily wash, wiping its legs thoroughly and methodically. Very slowly the grass snake slid forward, its head upturned and its eyes fixed on the bluebottle, which—realising the danger in time—flew off and disappeared among the heather, moss, and undergrowth. The grass snake sank back and relaxed, dozing in the warmth of the spring sun.

Over on the other side there was another grass snake, and in among the twigs to the right yet a third, and among the liverworts there were more, two, three, four—an enormous one among them. It seemed to be " snakes day " in Old Kare's garden. As the blackbird saw the grass snake's head, it started chattering incessantly, the bullfinch interrupted its whistle as a frightened snake slid through the brushwood. But the hazel hen seemed more frightened than anything else. It was dozing off when it was awakened by a light rustle. Looking up it was face to face with the snake. Struck by fear it jumped into the air, wings trembling, followed by a shower of soil and fine dust, before rushing to a low pine for shelter. The grass snake seemed to be just as frightened as it curled itself up and remained quite motionless.

The sun warmed the spring day. Buds on the lime tree swelled and the bird cherry seemed ready to burst. Stiff stems of wild raspberry pushed their way through the dead leaves, while the baneberry started germinating down among the brushwood. The shrew looked for grubs among the lichens, and a yellow butterfly fluttered around and settled on an aspen twig, spreading its wings out to blend in with the yellow-veined leaves.

The whole world seemed to be coming to life again, the bitter cold of winter a thing to be forgotten, and the air was full of the sounds of life, and a promise of warm summer days to come.

In spring Old Kare's garden
seethes with life. The whole world
is celebrating the end of the long
winter, and the approach of warm
summer days. The goldcrest darts
to and fro among the hanging
foliage, and down below the hazel
hen enjoys a bath in the warm soil.

The sound of dogs

It was difficult for Enok to follow the charcoal-burners' track once he had turned at the western end of the slope. It wound its long way up towards the clearing on the northern side where the capercailzie usually displayed. The wood was dense, and large holes made by woodpeckers gaped down—large dead pines lay across the track. The May night was at its darkest just now ; it was cold and clear. The swamp was still frozen over and the air was heavy with the smell of damp earth, and in some of the denser parts of the forest light patches of ash-grey snow showed up in the darkness.

Enok was not the only one who took advantage of the thickness of the trees and the darkness of the nights to venture forth in the very early hours, gun in hand, in search of capercailzie. Anders had been on the warpath night after night for the last three weeks, and some of the other foresters had begun to realise that roast capercailzie was very tasty indeed.

They all knew quite well, of course, that the capercailzie was protected—particularly during the mating and breeding season— but that merely added the spice of danger to these exploits of the early hours, and made the unfortunate capercailzie taste all the better. In any case there was no one to enforce the game laws where the foresters were almost the only people about—though it was well known that the head forester took his duties seriously, and included in his duties a care for the wild life in his area.

Enok heard a short clear bark echo from down near the edge of the swamp. He stopped and listened, puzzled at the sound. He felt uncertain and held his breath. No, it was nothing, maybe an owl or a moorhen stricken with spring fever.

Cautiously he continued on his way, listening as he went. Then he heard the same sound again, about the same distance away and just as difficult to locate. The sound was quick and short, rather like that of a dog on a leash pulling to get away. He stopped again to think and listen.

A long *hoo-hoo* from the eagle owl echoed in a deep dreary note. At the sound of the owl Enok calmed down and continued along the winding path for a few yards. Then he heard three clear barks in quick succession, clearer and more agitated—nearer and nearer the sound seemed to come.

76

A shiver ran down his back as he took a deep breath and drew himself up. He thought it sounded rather like the head forester's dog when it was kept on the leash, or when it scented an elk just before it was let loose. He knew that the head forester was a conscientious man, and that he might well be up in this district to see whether any tree stumps had been cut too high or whether any wood had been forgotten under the snow. It was even possible that he had heard shots in the early mornings when Anders had been out after the courting capercailzie night after night.

Enok listened again and grew nervous and uneasy. Next time he heard the barking he did not stop, but increased his speed instead, running down the path and jumping between the trees like a shadow, nimbly and softly, quiet as a mouse. But the quicker he moved, the closer and more enraged the barking seemed to get. It drove him on while his thoughts ran riot.

" The head forester is quite old, it is impossible for him to keep up the pace, even though he is being pulled along by his dog ; his sight is bad, and he can't see in the dusk. By rights he ought to be a good way behind now, but perhaps he has let the dog off the leash, perhaps it is hunting and chasing me. In that case it will be on me any moment now, and it is a strong bad-tempered beast. If I try to run away, I shall get the dog's teeth in my back ; then I shall have to shoot the animal and run for my life. Run home to my cottage and go to bed and deny everything when the head forester comes. Surely I shall be able to get away with it, I have always been on good terms with him ? But if I do that, Anders will be blamed and strife and unfriendliness will follow. Anders will do everything in his power to malign me and there will be a row in the village shop, it will be in all the papers. The peace of the woods will be turned to hell. No, I must manage some other way, I must confuse the dog, dodge it by jumping aside, or by wading up the stream for some distance."

Near the clearing he jumped off the path into the bilberry bushes, and, jumping from tussock to tussock, made a wide detour. The barking followed, came closer and sounded more aggravated and hoarser than before. Enok was now convinced that the dog was free. Wet and sticky with sweat, he realised that the wind was against him and would carry his scent.

If only he had stayed at home and left Anders alone among the cocks ! But the fishing had been bad ; the pike in the lake had played under the ice and the small nets which he cast round the edges of the water when the ice started melting were empty. His meat was finished,

The mating season approaches. Morning and evening the capercailzie cock displays, but he keeps his eyes wide open and alert.

Pages 80, 81 and 83.

Farther down the ural owl has hatched her eggs. She flies around while her mate sits on a stump, until one of the young appears at the hole to survey its future hunting ground.

and flour made him feel sick and he did not intend going down to the village until next week, when he could go to the head forester to collect his wages.

Jumping from tussock to tussock Enok ran over the boulders like a mountain goat. He jinked too and fro like a hare, dodging right and left, but it was all in vain. The barking got louder and nearer. As he heard the *tjut, tjutt, tjutt, tjitt, tjitt* of the dwarf owl, a shiver ran down his back. When a fox barked impatiently, the sweat poured down his face. The owl continued to call and the barking drew nearer.

Enok gave in and jumped behind an old dry tree, its branches silhouetted against the morning sky. He loaded his gun, raised it and waited, his heart beating as though it would burst. Suddenly a large bird—an eagle owl—landed on one of the lower branches of the tree behind which he was hiding. The owl looked at him with its deep black eyes and called hoarsely three times in succession.

Here, blinking at him vacantly and barking at him from the branch just above his head, was the furious " dog " who had trailed him so skilfully through the wood !

" Stupid creature ! " Enok muttered, as he raised his gun and took aim. Putting his finger on the trigger he fumbled, and then remembered that a shot would disturb the capercailzie cocks. After all, the eagle owl hadn't really done him any harm—it was only restless trying to protect its eggs.

But he was annoyed with himself. He had heard the call of the eagle owl before in spring and on summer nights, and he should have recognised it. Shivering with cold he collected some twigs to make a fire. Just as he was about to light the fire a twig cracked nearby, and outlined against the sky he could see the figure of a man with a pointed fur cap carrying a gun, making his way to the clearing.

It was Anders—no one else had a fur cap like that. Enok was furious. He decided that he must do something desperate, for Anders had had enough birds during the past week or so, and today he could do without a cock.

After Anders had passed eastwards, Enok imitated a courting cock ; he could do it well, better than anyone else. He watched Anders, saw him stop and cup his hands behind his ears to listen. Enok continued to make capercailzie noises. He watched Anders turn and creep back, then he took cover and moved in towards the thicker wood. He was unable to see Anders any longer, but now and then he heard a branch crack.

Enok finished his " call ", and hurried up to the clearing where the real cocks were courting, reaching the place unseen and unheard. With the growing dawn the cocks were well under way ; one of them seemed quite crazy with the joys of spring, prancing and gurgling like a stream in spate.

Quickly and silently he made his way forward, watching the bird up on a branch where it sat with its tail fanned and wings hanging relaxed, neck outstretched. It was the work of a moment or two for Enok to stalk the bird, take aim, and fire.

At the sound of the shot all the cocks flew away, except one which

79

fell heavily to the frozen earth. Enok jumped forward and stuffed the bird into his bag, and then crept back to the thicket at the edge of the swamp. Not far from the eagle owl's nest he turned and went into the wood, stopping and listening as he went. He took the bird from his bag, flayed it, cut its head and limbs off, concealing them in the moss. Then he removed the heart and entrails, putting them on a flat stone close to the owl's nest, and—stuffing the body back into his bag—went on his way.

The owl flew down, barking no longer, but a metallic clicking sound echoed as its beak hit the stone. After a few moments the owl shook itself with a satisfied air, ruffled its feathers, coughed and gurgled.

In spite of its repulsive eating habits, the eagle owl is rather a fine looking bird. The feathers on its back are an odd mixture of autumn tints—dark brown and russet intermingling with paler shades while its neck feathers are creamy-white. Its most startling feature, however, is almost certainly its large piercing flame-coloured eyes, which—together with the tufts of feathers above its ears—endow it with a rather formidable appearance, which is at the same time a little sardonic and disdainful.

Quickly but silently Enok made his way back through the forest. It was easy for anyone who did not know the district to get lost here, for one tree looked much like another and there was little to distinguish one hillock from another.

He was just a little afraid that the head forester might have heard the shot, so he made as little noise as possible. Now and then he stopped and listened, but no sound of man was to be heard. All was not still, however, for the forest was full of noises—night noises from the owls, and day noises from a world awakening as the first rays of sunlight filtered through the trees.

Early morning in early spring is perhaps the most wonderful time in the forest. The cruelty of nature is of course still there, but it seems to be hidden by the beauty of the world. Everything seems to be touched with a sort of magic, as the sun lights up the tops of the trees, and makes the bright patches of green and red moss in the clearings even more brilliant.

The morning mist was rising among the trees and the dwarf owl continued whistling, the fox barked and the black grouse could be heard from the swamp. Crossing the edge of the swamp Enok could just hear the eagle owl—now its call had a dull heavy tone, not at all frightening.

82

The cranes and the fox

Farther down, where the hill slopes down to the bog, the wood is tangled and wild, with clear patches where the trees have been blown down by the gales—where dry trees creak and the overgrown stumps cower like spirits. Down there it is always dark.

The owl lives in a stump at the edge of the swamp, in an old hole where a branch used to be. Her hole offers her an open view over the whole bog. In spring nights when the thaw has set in she would sit listening to the rising cackle of the frogs as they play with one another, now and again lifting their heads above the surface of the pool. In the early mornings she would see the elks splashing in the pools round the cranberry-covered tussocks shiny with dew.

Indeed, the owl saw a great deal of what was going on in the world—as she sat motionless on her perch in the old tree. During the winter she had watched a strange combat between the fox and the eagle owl—both of them, of course, were dependent on the same rather limited food supply. Neither had been the victor, though a great deal of fur and feathers had been expended before the fox slank off into the undergrowth, and the eagle owl glided silently away though the trees, sweeping by like some eerie shadow.

A large woodpecker had chosen a nearby aspen to build its nest. Of course the continuous hacking and short slapping of wings and the shrill warning cries disturbed the owl, but nevertheless they were good neighbours. When the owl was hatching her eggs she heard the woodpecker calling—*Kyck-yck-yck* ! *Kyck-yck-yck* !—and would go up to her hole, still rather sleepy and dazzled by the light, but curious to see what was happening.

She could hear the sound of wings, and sensed rather than saw two parallel streaks flash past, one larger than the other. Then as her eyes got used to the light she saw the hawk attack the black grouse, miss and tear some feathers out. The black grouse fell like a stone straight down into the shrubbery near a thick pine. Thudding down to the ground, it took on the colour of the brushwood and twigs and disappeared from sight. The hawk swooped down in vain, flew up into a pine and looked down, its eyes burning and breast beating. It turned its neck this way and that, scanning the ground beneath with its piercing eyes, but the black grouse lay quite still, invisible amid the grey-brown earth, while its feathers floated down softly from

84

the sky. Disappointed, the hawk flew away like a shadow, followed by the excited chatter of the woodpecker.

The owl stared down at the brushwood where the grouse had vanished, put her head on one side, nodded and blinked a few times. As nothing more seemed to be happening, she blinked more slowly until she rolled back into the nest, leaving the hole empty once more—gaping, black, mysterious.

The owl is also wakened from her sleep or her daydreaming from time to time by the excited chatter of squirrels as they play in the branches overhead, leaping from tree to tree. She is not averse to a meal of squirrel herself when mice and voles are scarce, but it is not nearly so easy to catch a squirrel. They are pretty lively little creatures, quick to drop out of reach, and always keeping an eye open for trouble. They have to, for it is only their speed of movement and nimble agility amongst the tree tops that preserves them from martens, owls, and sparrow hawks !

But it was not only the woodpeckers' cries and the noisy chatter of squirrels that would bring the owl out of her hole. Just as often cranes out on the swamp would wake her and fill her with curiosity. Sometimes they started their deafening cry quite suddenly and unexpectedly, and the air seemed to quiver when they ceased. Sometimes they would call in the evenings or at night, mostly however in the early mornings, just as the mist closed in round their eggs like a thick opaque wall. It was then that life became most dangerous for these shy birds.

The cranes had lived on the swamp for as long as could be remembered. Every year they chose their nesting place just as carefully and relieved each other when hatching their eggs. Sometimes their eggs were washed away by the late spring floods, or the birds had to fight with fox cubs that had ventured too near.

A ditch ran across the swamp. In spring it was full and swollen and in summer and winter it was often dry. Just now the ditch was flooded. There was still a little frost in the moss, making the ground too hard to absorb the water, which had collected in little pools round the tussocks. The cranes had chosen one of the tussocks near the ditch for their nest. It was a large nest, made of straw and dead grass from the previous year, and in the middle of the nest there were two long white eggs, lying in a hollow.

The eggs are hatched by both parent birds, and it is remarkably difficult to distinguish male and female ; at a distance they look exactly alike. The broody crane is lazy and slovenly, pecking at the grass

85

roots around the water. Should a buzzard call high up in the sky, it will nod its head and blink, and if a snipe flops down at the edge of the water with outstretched wings, it will draw its head back, its beak protruding like a spear. The crane will watch the snipe, slightly amused and slightly offended, then it will doze off again. But it is only an apparent doze ; the owl knows that and has seen it proved several times, as an inexperienced young fox has been chased away from the swamp by screeching cries and beating wings.

One morning when the eggs were more than half hatched, the mist and the fox came together just at a time when both the cranes had left the eggs for a short while. That morning the owl was sitting on an old black branch only a few yards from the nest, seeing and hearing everything.

Coming over from the wood the vixen took cover behind a birch bush and then crept stealthily through the heather and dead grass. Aided by the rapidly encircling mist, she crept on. The vixen had never seen the cranes' eggs, but she knew exactly where they were and how many there were. Keeping pace with the mist, creeping through the dewy grass, she approached the nest. She had seen both the cranes go and knew that the nest was unguarded. She knew that it must be now or never.

The tussocks gave poor cover, but the increasing mist swirled around her and the golden fur blended in with the frost covered grass. Nearer and nearer she crept—she could smell the nest and the crane spillings, and the vision of eggs lured her on.

Then suddenly, there on the tussock surrounded by water, she saw something white. The eggs were lying in front of her, large and nourishing, an ideal meal for the young cubs back in the lair. Jumping carefully into the nest, the vixen took one egg and then the other, having a little difficulty with the second one. Her mouth was too full, so she tried again, slowly and carefully. The eggs were warm and her mouth watered.

Suddenly the alarm sounded. A shrill trumpeting cut through the May morning air, large wings beat through the mist like heavy black screens. The vixen was driven out over the swamp, jumping over the ditch, running criss-cross under the attack of beating wings. She received a dig in her side and stumbled, breaking one egg. Then she was struck by a hard wing and was thrown over, breaking the second egg and letting the contents flow out over the tussock. Long beaks stabbed at her from all sides, wings beat her. The vixen was tossed like a ball between them, wet and dirty, receiving blows and jabs

The owl lives in a wide crack down by the swamp. Returning from hunting it brakes with outstretched wings and stops at the hole.

from all directions, whining and yelping, her upper lip curled. She dared not stay, and her counter-blows were blind and weak. Not until she reached the undergrowth on the far side of the swamp could she take cover and disappear.

Her cubs would have to go hungry that day. Things were really getting desperate, for their tiny ribs were showing through their fur, and their appetites seemed to be insatiable. She had brought them frogs and the occasional mouse, but she needed far more nourishing food to satisfy those cubs, and enable their growing bodies to acquire the strength which they would need when they came to fend for themselves—which she hoped would be soon.

The vixen rested for a while in the shrubbery, sore, bedraggled, and exhausted, then slowly slunk back to her lair where she was welcomed with yelps of reproof and disappointment.

Over the swamp the trumpeting echoed on, filled with sorrow and despair at the high price of victory.

On a spring morning the cranes are to be found grazing on stubble patches, calling to each other and mating. A few weeks later it is time to build a nest and lay eggs among the tussocks on the marsh.

The eggs hatch after a month and the chicks seek the protection of the wood. They grow remarkably quickly and snap at flies and midges, plucking them out of their down.

No other bird in the wood is so fearless and brave as the jay. She sits and watches the camera with interest, and without showing the least sign of alarm.

Evening in the haunted wood

To the north of the Black Hill the ground was boggy and covered with moss. The wood was thin; the pines were low and stunted, old trees creaked and groaned and dead trees stood up as ghostly shadows against the sky. The wood was dark, and almost seemed haunted.

Neither daylight nor darkness reigned, but in the gathering dusk a soft glow of sunlight filtered obliquely through the gaunt pines, laying an intricate mosaic on the floor of the forest. This was the time when magic reigned in the forest, when one might well have the feeling that witches and warlocks abounded in and around the trees on all sides.

The air was filled with the buzz and hum and chatter of life, broken spasmodically by the calling of the owls. Now and then a twig would snap as a fox passed on his evening round, or as a doe returned from her drink at the river. The early morning too was full of the noises of life, but this was different. Then the very air of the forest was agog with the joy and the promise of a new day—now there was an air of mystery abroad, a mild threat of danger lurking not so very far away.

In an old dark tree stump a female willow tit cleared out her nest, while her mate hopped around among the twigs, calling continually : *Tji-tji-taah-taah, taah* ! *Tji-tji-taah-taah, taah* ! A shrew had made a network of tunnels under a drooping pine, and burrowing here and there it had made tiny bumps in the moss covering. At the edge of the moor a willow grouse had laid her eight speckled eggs, and in the evening stillness the cock called down from his look-out post on a moss stone : *Kav, kav, ka-haah, ha-haah, ha-aah* ! *Kavau* ! *Kavau* ! Otherwise the wood lay silent.

No, perhaps not quite silent ! Between two low pines there lay a tiny woven nest, lined with grouse down. Hidden among the black lichen it looked empty and abandoned. This was the spot which the Siberian jay had chosen for its nest.

It was evening at the jay's nest. The fledglings were big and would soon be able to fly. They had just been fed and were lying pressed close

Even the young jays seem quite fearless. They open their mouths as soon as anything moves nearby, waiting impatiently in the cold wind. But when fed and warm they can also enjoy the comfort and security of their nest.

together ; now and then one of them would stir, stand up and stretch, and then doze off again. In a nearby tree the parent bird sat watching them, ruffling himself up, so that his brown-grey breast and rust-coloured flanks blended with the lichens. When the wind fell and the air was quite still, he would start singing a low soft song, whistling and chirping at times. His song was a combination of the busy chatter of the songthrush and the melancholy babble of the robin, but it was soft and low, and sometimes could hardly be heard at all. At odd intervals he stretched his neck to have a look at his young, then dozed off again.

If the sun should get too warm, the jay would stop singing and jump up on the twig, standing firmly and shaking his feathers, leaving only a long tail and shiny black head in a ball of feathers. Feeling better, he would then continue his song. As the sun sank he would fly over to another pine to search for food. Cock and hen would meet on the ground hop around together, beating their wings and shaking their tails, bumping into each other until the cock coughed up a small ball of food, which the hen would take to the chicks.

When their evening flirt was over the sun would sink below the horizon, leaving the night to grow colder. The sky glowed in a greenish-yellow hue, and the grass whitened with frost. The mother jay sat at the edge of her nest, looking around, ruffling her feathers before creeping down again to spread her wings over her young. Later in the evening two tiny black beaks might appear from under each wing.

With the increasing darkness the cock would return to the nest with more food for his family. Cocking his head on one side, he checked that everything was in good order before flying up to his branch for the night.

The night fell silently, but it was cold—bitterly cold.

That was the surprising thing about those long spring nights. The days were so bright and warm and glorious, full of the promise of the long summer to come, that it was hard for the new life which was coming into being day after day to survive the long hours of bitter cold.

A bear visits the forest

The Devil's Stream in the narrow gorge between the two hills lives up to its name. Wildly it forces its way over rocks and through overgrown alder and willow, birch and pine, winding its way between moss covered boulders, disappearing at times, then appearing again frothing and rumbling. Down by the mire it flows more slowly as it widens to form pools covered with water lilies and the surface is broken by leaping trout, causing ripples that distort the reflected clouds. In some places the bank is muddy, making the stream dangerous, both to humans and animals.

One May morning when the birch leaves were about the size of a mouse's ear, and the sun was shining down on the mire, a large body lay damming up one of the pools like a soft mossy tussock. It was a dead elk, a young animal that had gone down to the stream and had been unable to climb back up the muddy bank. It was drowned and had been lying in the stream for two days.

Occasionally a bear would prowl round the mire—an old bear, its fur nearly black, with plenty of experience of the stream and its hazards. It was one of the bears that stayed in the wood to the north and visited the owl's wood at spring, tearing up anthills and eating any berries left from the previous year, always in search of any dead animals.

There were not so many bears left in the forest nowadays, as there had been in former years. As the foresters advanced—slowly but relentlessly—the bears had to move farther and farther north. Bears could never be thick on the ground, for they are by nature lazy creatures, spending their lives eating and sleeping and food is not plentiful. They live on bees' and wasps' nests and wild berries—and a bear has to cover a great deal of ground to find enough of these to satisfy it, day after day and week after week. Occasionally it may manage to catch a fish from the stream or one of the many ponds and lakes that abound in the forest, and sometimes a bear may be observed lying for hours on end on the banks of a river, or on a large rock or

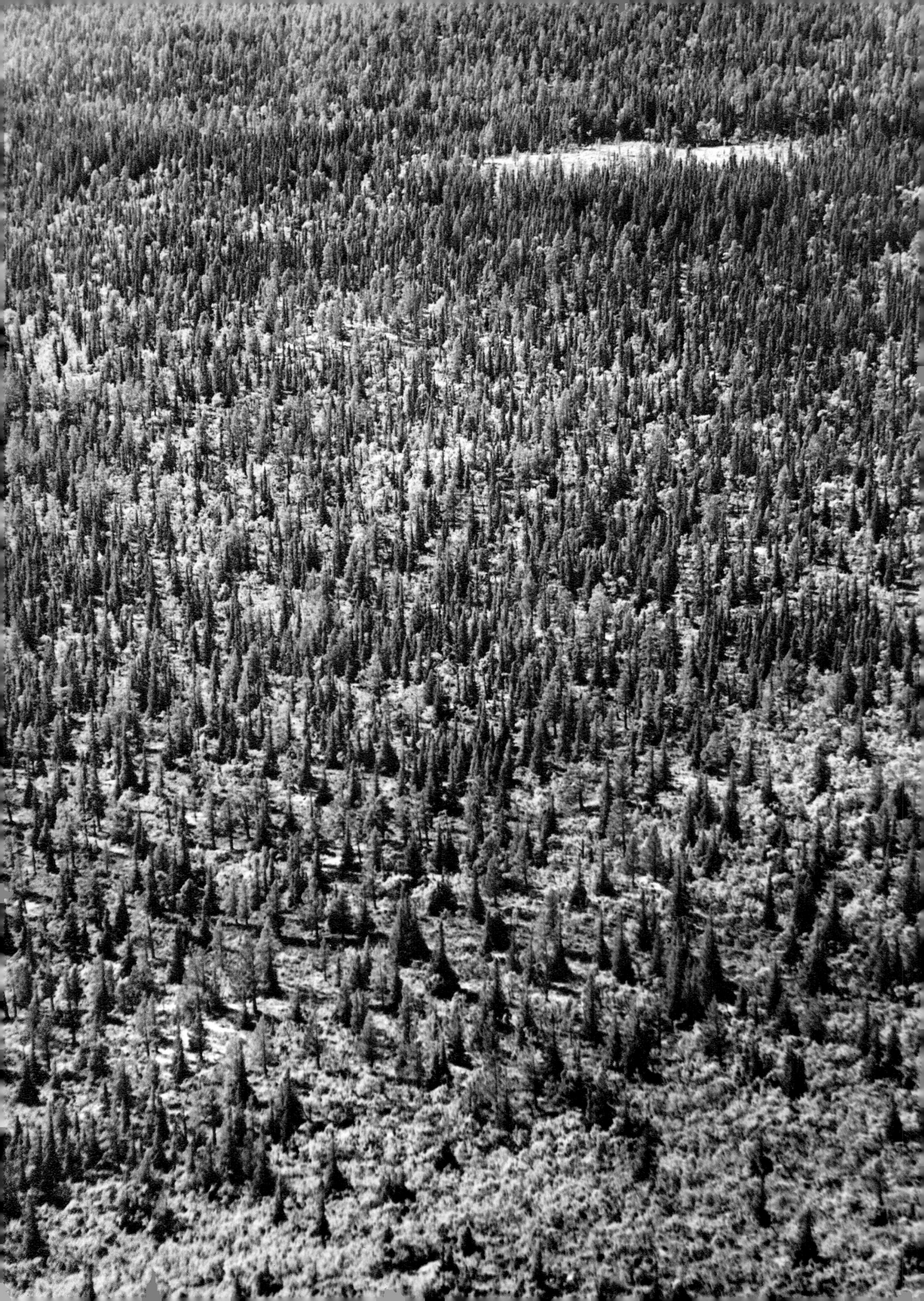

Hunting is no longer a necessity for those dwelling in the wood, and old traps and shelters are gradually rotting away. Not so very long ago hunting was the only means of livelihood for the people who lived in these forests.

boulder at the edge of a lake, its eyes glued on the water as it waits patiently for an opportunity to grab.

But if a bear finds a dead animal lying in the forest, this is a god-sent opportunity for a feast—and it is not often that a bear can gorge itself for days on end without going to the trouble of having to find its food, or gather berries laboriously from a wide area.

And so it came about this May morning that the old black bear snuffled the air with dilated nostrils, its eyes bright with excitement. It could scent the dead elk a long way off. Raising its head, it would sniff and listen, and then make its way straight across the mire to the stream. It did not take it long to find the elk, and it inspected and sniffed the dead animal thoroughly before it crawled down into the mud. Spreading its paws out to prevent itself from sinking, the bear went down on its haunches and pushed the elk, causing the body to heave in the mud. Sniffing and grunting the bear stretched out a paw to get hold of the elk's hind leg and tried to pull it. Leaning forward it bit and pulled, but only sank deeper into the mud. It threw itself back, trying to get a new grip on the elk, but only sank into the mud again.

Pulling and pushing the bear tried to move the elk into deeper water, but it stumbled in the muddy water. Throwing itself back, it tried again, splashing and stumbling, but without success as it was impossible to find a firm foothold.

The bear grew excited and grunted in anger. It rose up out of the water, beating its paws and splashing water and mud over its wet fur. As is common among bears when they require a sudden spurt of energy, it rushed up to a young tree, climbed up it quickly and gracefully, breaking off twigs and tearing the bark, higher and higher until the tree bent and broke under the weight. As it fell with a heavy thud the bear got even crosser. Rushing at the elk it dragged it up a little way, then sank in, but finding a firmer foothold it finally managed to drag the dead animal up.

It rested for a while, looked around, and then dragged the dead elk backwards, pulling it towards some trees, but the elk kept catching on sharp stones. The bear beat its chest with rage, then rushed into the wood and collected an armful of brushwood and heather and filled up the holes until there was a smooth path for it to drag the elk along. Having dragged the body up to the pines, the bear began its repulsive feast, accompanied by the chatter of the thrush and the inquisitive willow tit as they flew from tree to tree. The jay had brought

104

her fledglings out for the first time and came to inspect the proceedings, tempted by the lavish supply of food.

The bear enjoyed its feast for days on end. The body of the dead elk grew smaller and smaller as the dark heaps of bear spillings grew. Between meals the bear would lie and rest under one of the pines on a bed of soft moss. Now and then it chased foxes and hawks away, but it was quite willing to share its prize with the jays and tits. After every meal it would bury the meat in a deep hollow, covering it carefully with moss, but sometimes it ate so much that it could only manage to pull up the moss lying nearby to cover the meat, before it crawled to its mossy bed to digest the food, lulled to sleep by the distant barking of the fox and the soft singing of the eagle owl, the hawk's cry or the hammering of the woodpecker, or perhaps by the incessant murmur of the Devil's Stream and the sandpiper's cry echoing across from the bog.

The meat lasted for about a week. The bones were scraped clean and the heaps of spillings formed a circle round the banqueting scene. The moss was torn up and there were deep gashes and scrapes on the trees, with a well-trodden path leading from the moss to the hollow. On the following morning the bear buried the skeleton for the last time, covered it with moss, rolled a few stones on top of it and then went over to the stream for a drink before making its way northwards to the thicker parts of the forest. Over there on more familiar ground there was more hope of finding a mate, now that it was satisfied and strengthened for any love affair.

The mating season is but a brief interlude in the annual round of a bear. The male bear has a short spell of connubial zeal, but this passes off soon enough when the young ones arrive, and the female is left with all the cares and worries of bringing up the family—finding food for herself and a pair of ravenous youngsters, and protecting them from the numerous dangers which threaten the lives of all young creatures in the forest.

Man was not yet a serious danger in this part of the forest, though the bears kept well out of sight if they could. It is a doubtful privilege to be one of the largest animals in the forest, and to be obliged to keep on the move in order to remain alive.

Rose of the heath

After the last snowdrifts had disappeared from the northern side of the Black Hill and the muddy waters of the spring flood had subsided, peace returned to the wood once more. The capercailzie cock lost its lust to fight, the hens started laying eggs and hatching them. The grouse played no longer, the gurgling sounds became irregular and their calls seemed empty and pointless.

So it goes on in the forest, year after year. As the harsh struggle of winter gives way gradually to longer days and warm air in place of the biting fury of the preceding months, all life becomes involved in a crescendo of sound and joy and zest for living and breeding, which reveals itself in countless different ways.

Then as the days become still longer and warmer, a sort of anticlimax sets in. The wooing and mating is past, and life settles down once more to the dull round of breeding, feeding, and protecting the young and defenceless. And so as spring turns into early summer and early summer to midsummer, the tempo of life seems to slow down, the sounds are silenced or become less urgent.

The last patches of snow had hardly disappeared before light places showed up among the trees, rather like old snow bespattered with pine needles, untouched by the sun. But this was not snow, it was the wood anemone, or rose of the heath as it was commonly called in the forest. Tiny buds shot up from among the leaves, sprawling about as though drunk with sleep. The buds swelled and grew large and round, and turned pale pink at the base before making a final effort to shake off sleep and then burst open. Turning towards the sun, the petals followed it from east to west, swaying and dancing in the wind, soaking in all the warmth until the outer edges of the petals bent and turned brown. The anemones endowed the dry twigs with life. In their modest beauty, they are one of the most lovely things in the forest. Every night they close up to shelter from the cold, looking like hairy brown buds again, hardly visible among the brushwood.

These anemones used to be found almost everywhere, but since the tracks were made into the wood, people came there digging up everything until many of the rightful forest dwellers disappeared. People picked the anemones, fought for the best flowers, and took roots and plants ; weak and sensitive buds were damaged. Everyone wanted the flower, and it was picked and ravaged until it practically disappeared. Finally it had to be protected.

On a barren stony slope among heather and bilberries it was still to be seen—a large shining white patch of flowers, gleaming like a snowfield. A capercailzie hen had laid her eggs under one of the clusters on the hill, the buds swelled and burst and left the hen lying amid a honey-scented clump of flowers.

One evening the old vixen made her way over the hill, straight towards the bush. It was a calm and warm evening, the anemones were in full flower. The vixen stopped at the edge of the flowers hesitated a while and then turned away. It seemed as though she did not dare enter the mass of flowers. The hen lay quite still until the vixen had passed—the flowers had saved her life, and her brood.

The following day a butterfly flew along the south slope of the hill, small and dainty, humming softly as it went. It could hardly be seen among the brushwood, and when it landed on a mossy stone it blended beautifully with its surroundings ; but sitting on the yellow stamens of the flower it seemed enormous. The robin saw it and flew down towards it and snapped it up. Sitting on a nearby stone the robin swallowed its meal and clapped its beak as it took another scrutinising look at the flowers.

The anemone is the main flower of the forest. There are many other flowers, of course, and a botanist would be kept busy for a very long time in the spring and early summer, when tiny spots of colour spring up everywhere in the wake of the retreating snow. But none is so lovely—so pure and so delicate—as the rose of the heath, the anemone that seems to welcome and draw one on into the thicker parts of the forest.

It is really quite amazing the number of unexpected surprises to be found, if you really use your eyes and look well about you when walking through the forest. The most unlikely objects acquire an air of real, almost ethereal beauty. Even a snail—not generally considered as one of nature's beauties—can be a thing of sheer loveliness if you examine it closely, and marvel at the wonderful spiral of its shell, and delicate regular pattern of its skin.

108

There are all sorts of flowers in owl's wood, but anemones are the most common, white and welcoming.

The snail is a timorous creature, but not without its own rather unusual beauty.

The house in the aspen tree

Throughout the whole world each animal, bird, and insect finds shelter in a home which it has built for itself, or which providence has provided. For the rose-chafer there is the heart of the rose ; for the young swift—sleeping as it is said high among the clouds on a summer's night—there is all the immensity of the sky.

Most animals make their own homes, and some take infinite care and go to almost unbelievable trouble to make a home which is both beautiful and useful, comfortable and protective. Some animals, however, are by no means loath to enter into occupation of some other animal's discarded home. For instance, owl—squirrel—and woodpecker may well use the same hole in an old tree on successive years, or even during the same year. The hare or the grouse, on the other hand, is quite satisfied with a sort of hollow amidst the grass or the heather, and takes little trouble to embellish or fortify the home— or even to stake any long-term claim to it.

There is the penduline tit, who works extremely hard for about twelve days to build a beautiful, intricate, and comfortable home of twig and bushwood, sheep's wool, and stringy fibre from reeds. It is the male bird's job to do the actual building, and the female is responsible for furnishing the home with the softest and finest material she can find.

At the other end of the scale, many animals—among them red deer, roe deer, wild pigs—make their lairs in a shallow hole in the bracken or heather, or under the trees or a carpet of moss and leaves.

A great many animals live in holes in the ground which they have to dig and develop for themselves. Many of these, of course, spend the greater part of the winter hibernating in their holes.

In the animal world change of tenancy is suprisingly frequent. Wolverines, pumas, and other hunters who like to wait for their prey for hours on end are often temporarily resident in clefts and holes, but they have no domestic instincts and prefer to live by themselves. A home may well pass from animal to animal—being abandoned by one animal and patched up by another—but cases of plain robbery may also occur in nature. The fox is a good digger and can excavate a comfortable dwelling with its claws, but it must be confessed that it

is also prone to stealing other animals' homes—particularly the well-kept dwelling of the badger. Sometimes fox and badger even occupy different parts of the same home—but never for long !

Owls—particularly the smaller varieties—usually favour holes in trees, though they may also inhabit holes in walls, quarries, or ruined buildings, or even disused rabbit burrows. Wherever it is, it is generally near their favourite perching branch. Let us now take a look at a pair of pigmy owls who lived in an aspen tree in our forest.

The pigmy owl was sitting high up in a tree, turning its head and scanning the surroundings with its sharp yellow eyes, whistling at regular intervals rather like the subdued piping of a bullfinch, only with more of a screech. It looked rather like a thrush, only shorter and not so smooth.

With a heavy tread an elk plodded through the wood, magnified unnaturally in the morning mist, looking rather like a shapeless shadow. The owl crouched down, its gaze sharpening, its tail pointing up at right-angles. Then, with undulating flight similar to that of a woodpecker, it followed the elk. Settling in another tree it could hear the scraping of hooves and the cracking of twigs, then it whistled. It whistled more harshly now with a more monotonous note, higher and more quickly.

The pigmy owl hen woke up and looked out from the hole on the northern side of the aspen tree, wondering what had happened. She turned her head and gazed through the mist.

The great spotted woodpecker had lived in the aspen the year before—in fact it was the woodpecker who had made the hole, which was cut at an upward angle to protect it from the rain and weather. Here the woodpecker had laid her eggs and reared her young, but her hole suited the pigmy owl admirably, so she took it.

As the thud of the elk's hooves died down and her mate's whistle became softer, the pigmy owl sank back over her newly hatched chicks.

A week later the chicks had grown considerably. Sometimes they whistled very softly and the owl's hen-like clucking could be heard as she busied herself with them. At regular intervals she would remove fluff and rat hairs from the nest, sitting at the opening for a while, well back at first with only one eye visible, then she would push her head out, turning her head jerkily and crouching down as a tree creeper climbed a branch nearby, and should a tit knock against the top of the tree, she would stretch her head out, keeping the fluff in her beak. Finally, she would open her beak, almost absent-mindedly, and let the fluff float down to the moss at the foot of the aspen, where dead leaves and the shells of the five eggs were already covered with a downy bluish-grey blanket. Blinking sleepily she would then go back into her nest.

Towards evening things got more lively around the aspen. More and more often the pigmy owl looked out ; tits called to each other, the flycatchers chased flies, and thrushes chattered. When she heard her mate calling with a long drawn-out note, she would answer with a quick repeated chatter. Shortly afterwards her round face would appear at the hole, whistling and chattering more sharply than her mate. He approached carrying a long-tailed field mouse between his claws, whistling and chuckling as he flew. The hen flew out to him up in the pine and he fluttered round her, the mouse hanging down. She flung herself at him and took the mouse from him. For a while the birds played, whistling and knocking against each other, then with the mouse between her claws the hen returned to her hole in the aspen, sliding softly through the hole and drawing the mouse in with her, letting its tail sweep against the walls of the hole. Then the meal began amid excited chatter. The mouse did not last long, but disappeared quickly into hungry mouths. The hen owl came up several times with a bunch of fur to the exit from the hole, always listening before she let the fur glide down to the ground. Then she waited, expecting more food.

An hour passed.

Crouched down she stretched her beak out now and again and watched a tit pass by, and when a shrew fought its way through the brushwood, squeaking impatiently, she looked down and watched but she did not go after it.

Her mate had been away a long time, he must have been delayed. None of the other birds gave warning of his approach, the June evening was quiet and sleepy. The pigmy owl grew impatient and jumped up and down in the hole. Suddenly she hurled herself out and flew to a nearby tree to survey the land, then disappeared into a hole and was out again quickly with a stiff, cold willow tit in her claws. Pulling the tit up under her body, she flew down to her nest. A second meal followed with renewed chattering and piping ; then the nest was cleaned out again.

After cleaning the nest the pigmy owl hen sat at the hole, watching and waiting. Another hour passed and still the cock had not returned. She flew out again, impatient and nervous, crossing from tree to tree, looking and peering, holding her tail erect. In the dusk she rather resembled a busy young thrush. Finally she found a squirrel's nest

A week before midsummer the pigmy owl fledglings are ready to fly out. It is a busy time for the owl, and a dangerous one for voles, mice, and small birds.

When the owl returns with food, the hen goes to collect it from him, some distance from the nest. She goes to the hole in the aspen, dragging the vole behind her. Then the feast can begin.

and burrowed and dug in the twigs until she found a dead vole. With the vole held firmly in her claws, she flew straight down to her nest. That was the last meal for the evening so she did not bother to clean up nor to look out of her hole any longer.

Silence fell over the group of aspen trees. The woodcock went to its nest, down at the lake the tengmalm's owl cried and now and again the loud trumpeting of the cranes echoed out into the night. The churring of the nightjar sounded from the north. At midnight the woodcock settled down, passing like a dark shadow among the old leaves until it vanished in some twigs.

Daybreak came and the shadows faded. A song thrush started singing, imitating the coarse whistle of the pigmy owl and then pretending to be a barn owl or a crane. As the sun rose over the tops of the trees the woodpecker started drumming, softly at first, then more coarsely with a hollow note. The pigmy owl was not bothered by it, not even when her aspen tree quivered under its tapping—the woodpecker belonged there. Suddenly the tits grew restless, chirping and twittering, and then the long-drawn whistle of the pigmy owl echoed out above their warning calls.

The hen looked out but did not answer the call. She rushed up to a branch in the pine and met her mate, who had come back without any food. The little hen was furious and went for him, pecking and beating him with her wings. He accepted all his punishment, but seemed tired and was knocked down from the tree and chased out eastwards, where there was usually some hope of catching a vole. He whistled while she chattered like an angry fieldfare. Only when he was out over the clearing did she return, puffed up with rage and her eyes glaring. The cock took his time, while the hen sat and chattered at her hole. The rising sun warmed the earth, the dew dried and bird song increased. The woodcock lay in the sun between the roots, enjoying the warmth.

From the clearing the pigmy owl let out a happy victorious whistle. The hen flew out and reached the branch in the pine at the same time as her mate. The exchange of the loot was lively and the cock was pushed over to the next branch. The hen looked at the prize. Stiffening she stared and blinked several times. Her ruffled feathers sank together, she shrank back and stared and blinked at the object. A lizard ! A cold, dreadful lizard ! She stretched, making herself as narrow as possible for a pigmy owl, then taking the lizard in one claw and holding it out away from her, she opened her claw and let the animal drop.

116

The lizard fell, bumping from twig to twig as it went. The owl resumed her normal posture, but then stretched her head out to watch the lizard fall. Even after the lizard had disappeared among the sprigs of bilberry and heather, she sat and stared, amazed—almost frightened. Pulling herself together she then looked around and made her way back to the squirrel's nest and pulled out a field shrew almost as big as herself, and took it to her hole.

Shortly afterwards she was back in the pine, sitting there and ruffling her feathers as she cleaned herself, disregarding the warning cries around her, her short tail pointing up at right-angles. Then she relaxed and rested, warmed by the sun, and started whistling in a low key, rather like a bullfinch.

Her mate grew bored and moved in towards the trunk of the tree, pressing himself against the bark like a small invisible ball.

The old dead tree

There was an old dead tree where the bog edged down to the lake. Silhouetted against the sky it stood prominent like a lighthouse, visible from afar. It had a long twisted slender trunk, with a flattened top, its knotted branches reaching out like the fingers of an old man, frozen while outstretched begging for something.

The tree was lop-sided. On the side facing the lake there used to be an osprey's nest, well anchored amid the branches, but one autumn the branch broke and the nest was thrown down, falling into the bog with a heavy wet thud. The ospreys moved and the old tree rotted. Now and again a bird would return to the old tree, raise its head and ruffle up its feathers as it sat on one of the upper branches ; or maybe it would crouch down low, holding a pike between its claws.

Other birds also visited the old tree. Sitting there the buzzard would search for grass snakes or frogs, or the reed bunting would chirp as a kestrel alighted on the higher branches. Before starting to hunt, the eagle owl would rest on the lower branches, blinking sleepily. Sometimes its cry would echo from the old tree, piercing the air, while it sat silhouetted like a soft ball with two protruding horns in the light of the summer evening.

A few years ago the great black woodpecker made a large nesting hole in the middle of the trunk of the old tree, on the side facing the lake. That was a bad spring for the old tree. Rows of unfinished holes appeared on the trunk, and several branches were nearly stripped bare as the woodpecker's drumming echoed all round the wood. But the great black woodpecker only stayed there one year. The next lodger was the tengmalm's owl. In early spring it had already staked its claim, its hunting call echoing across the lake. By the time summer arrived there was not a single shrew left in the neighbourhood. This owl was not a clean bird and did not clean the hole out, so when its nest started sprouting it moved on.

Then the old tree remained deserted for two or three years, until the goldeneye took over.

It was at the end of April, the ice was just free of its mantle of snow, and would shortly turn a dirty bluish-grey ; but it was still thick and safe, and on the northern side of the wood there was still some snow left in the hollows. Out on the bog a small stream sparkled, where a small crack had opened in the ice, gradually growing larger and larger.

One morning three goldeneyes appeared on the clear stream, two drakes with white patches on their cheeks and a grey-brown duck with a white ring round the bottom of her neck. The drakes started courting, crossing the water towards the duck at a terrific speed. Gliding with wings half spanned they fanned out their tail feathers and puffed themselves up. Stopping abruptly in front of the duck they raised themselves up and threw their heads back, showing their breasts and white underfeathers in the morning sun. Sometimes they even bent their necks so far back that their heads touched their tails, before they threw their heads forwards again, quacking loudly and chattering. Their courting continued for a few days while the thaw spread to wood and stream, until the duck selected her drake and the loser flew off to the south.

A few weeks later the lake was clear of ice, and the pair of golden-eyes were out on the clear water. The duck had already chosen her nest a long time ago, and now and then she visited the woodpecker's deserted hole in the old tree ; sometimes her drake went with her, flying in across the lake. At the end of May the duck suddenly vanished. She had laid her eggs and only returned in the mornings and evenings, after having filled her crop with snails and grubs from the bottom of the lake. Now, having completed his job, the drake left the lake and went south to more familiar waters.

Summer was really here at last. A profusion of wild flowers of all sorts carpeted the floor of the forest, and surrounded the reed-encircled verge of the lake. Frogs croaked loudly all night long, and at dawn there was a chorus of small birds around, over, and on the surface of the lake, heralding vociferously the arrival of a new day.

At one end of the lake there was a cluster of willows, and these were decked with a newly acquired silky down of pussy willows, quivering and scintillating in the golden light. The air was filled with a hum of insect life, and in the evenings the continuous but spasmodic *plop plop plop* could be heard of trout leaping right out of the water, leaving behind them a series of circular ripples ever widening. These ripples are always intensely beautiful things—fascinating even—because they are always moving, always changing, and it is hard to tell when the ripples resulting from one particular trout's leap came to an end.

There were a few horse chestnuts in the forest—not many, but they could be seen from afar on account of their tall upright chandeliers of blossom. Hawthorns and blackthorns were clad in their mantles of blush pink and white, and countless small birds pecked wantonly at the blossom in their search for insects.

The wild cherry bloomed and the lily of the valley was in flower, birch leaves acquired a fresh shade of green, grass and reeds shot up. Young redpoll chicks flew about, the moorhen hatched her eggs, and the reed bunting had just finished laying. In a week's time it would be midsummer.

Then suddenly one night the first egg cracked open in the hole in the old tree. From under the soft down a small wet black creature appeared, squeaking softly, nestling into its mother's warm down trying to dry itself. One after another the chicks hatched, the hole was filled with a wet mass of black squeaking bodies. The duck made her way down to the lake in search of food and drink for her family. She was away for a long time and seemed nervous and impatient, and her anxiety increased towards evening.

Late at night, about twenty-four hours after the first chick was hatched, she went down into the brushwood and jumped around, calling her young. Just then a fox crept over the bog, stopped and listened to the duck's call and thought of the food it needed for its own young. Crouching and creeping the fox reached a hiding place in a bush just a few yards from the old tree. All around it could hear the duck's cries. Raising itself carefully on its haunches it saw the brushwood moving and heard the low call: *prah, prah, praah, praah*, then something came flying down through the air and landed, in the moss with a bump. Something black and fluffy had landed. Irritated and frightened the fox put its ears back and curled its upper lip, sinking down low. Looking about, the fox heard something chattering up in the old tree and saw a black ball peering down from the woodpecker's hole. Now it understood everything !

The goldeneye duck grew more eager in her call: *prah, prah, praah*. As it clambered out through the hole, the black ball got bigger until it filled the entire opening, nodded, then turned its head and followed its mother's call. With a bewildered squawk it jumped right out, its bare wings beating the air helplessly. The fox darted forward, but the brushwood was high and hid the young bird.

Changing her note, the goldeneye duck went off towards the swamp, giving a sharp short warning cry. The fox twisted and turned in the brushwood, he listened and sniffed till a shadow passed over and covered him and wide wings beat, while hard beaks pecked him furiously. The fox turned and fled in a zig-zag track towards the wood to take cover under the brushwood and twigs.

The eagle owl flew up to the old tree and sat on one of the lower branches, not far from the hole. Ruffling up its feathers it

When the young goldeneye is 24 hours old it has an uncontrollable urge to leave the safety of the nest. Climbing up it stands piping at the hole for a moment, then jumps out into the air, braking with its tiny wings and webbed feet before it falls in the grass. It does not take it long to find the protection of the water.

clicked its beak and uttered its short erratic cry. All other life was silent.

Next morning the fox ventured back to the old tree, back to the heather and scented bog-myrtle. Sniffing and scenting it followed the track down to the edge of the lake. Down there near an outlying tussock of reeds the clutch of goldeneye were busy in the water, ducking and splashing. Now the chicks were safe from the hawk and eagle owl and were beyond the reach of the fox and weasel—but they did not yet know of the old pike's fancy.

What a wonderful hide-out the reeds round the lake made for birds of all sorts. They were safe from attack from the air, as they could not easily be seen as long as they did not venture forth into the open waters of the lake. They were safe from prowling four-footed animals, who could not leave firm ground to explore among the recesses and thickets of the reeds. The enemy under the water was indeed a different problem, and only time could endow the young birds with size and speed to combat the treacherous assaults of the pike.

When the storm clouds gathered, and the waters of the lake were whipped up into fury by an angry wind, the trees round about would be bowed before the gale, and the ground below would be scattered with fir cones, leaves, and broken branches.

But dead old trees like the one selected by our family of goldeneyes can survive as gaunt bare figures in the forest for a great many years, and seem the only unchanging figures in a changing landscape.

Now that summer had really come to the forest, it was interesting to look back on the manner of its arrival. At first the signs had been a gradual lengthening of the hours of daylight, followed by spasmodic thawing and refreezing. As the thaw gained the upper hand, and the first vestiges of wild flowers appeared in the wake of the fast vanishing snow, the first mating call of birds could be heard, and the pines showed the little spots of silver or gold at the tips of their branches—like myriads of tiny spots of light in a dark room.

And then quite suddenly there had been a dramatic explosion of spring all over the forest—the scattered clusters of flowers had become a veritable carpet, trees had burst into new leaf, squirrels had chased each other vociferously through the branches, and the forest was suddenly teeming with life again. The winter had been long and hard, and many creatures had perished, but now the world was young again, and the whole summer lay ahead. Outside the tropics spring is always a glorious time, but never more so than in these northern forests, where life has been dormant for so long.

124

The troll tarn

Where the pine wood is thickest and where the golden maidenhair grows high and soft, there is a tarn sparkling like an eye in the blue haze of a summer evening. Sedges and rushes grow down to the shore of the tarn, and out in the clear water grass covered tussocks stand out like small islands. Cloudberry flowers show up against the maidenhair, and twisted birches grow on the slope. Down by the spring in a clearing between the pines there is a patch of lady's slipper ; the wind never finds its way down to the clearing, nor does the chattering of the stream disturb the silence.

Sometimes, however, the clear surface of the water is broken, usually in the mornings and evenings, although sometimes even at midday. After her eggs were hatched, the teal hen lived under a bush down by the tarn together with her chicks. A frog swam happily among the tussocks, red-bellied water lizards broke the surface, piercing tiny holes in it. In the morning haze water-boatmen would lie on the surface warming themselves, until—frightened by the sound of passing wings or a thirsty elk—they would scurry away. Down by the water a blackbird was washing its shiny feathers, while a doe quenched its thirst.

The variety of living creatures in and around the tarn was almost unbelievable. The mud at the bottom was crawling with the nymphs of insects that would later rise to the surface and leave the water on wings. Toads, frogs, and newts abode in large numbers amongst the reeds, and many of them would in time fall victim to the aquatic birds which either spent the summer on the tarn, or visited it from larger lakes of the forest.

The life below the surface was not often seen, but its existence was confirmed by the presence of a pair of otters, which appeared to fare quite well and flourish. Now and then Enok would appear and wander hopefully round the tarn with his rod, but the periphery of the tarn was so overgrown with reeds that fishing was by no means easy.

Plant life too showed an amazing expansion during the early weeks of the summer, water-lilies burst open their waxen cups, and pondweed spread through the shallow water in profusion.

The trees around the tarn were mainly pines, but at one end there was an open oak wood, and forming a fringe round both oak and pine there was a thin graceful circle of silver birches—their beautiful

bark gleaming with an intense golden light in the early morning and late evening, when the sun's rays shone obliquely through the trees, throwing long shadows and forming an intricate mosaic of light and shade, browns and golds and greens, against the duck-egg blue of the sky.

In June, when the sun beat down, a number of elks wallowed in the mud, horse-flies following them in a thick cloud. One evening an elk calf almost became stuck in the mud ; its hind legs sank in and the clammy muddy soil clung to its limbs like a thick glue. No doubt its hind legs had reached the bottom, but the mud was too deep and thick, holding the animal down. Frightened, the young elk thrust itself forwards and sideways, clawing with its hooves and throwing moss and dead grass up into the trees. The animal's eyes became strained and red, till suddenly it had an idea : struggling grimly towards the side it thrust its fore-legs out, dragging and pulling. Once, twice, three times it thrust its legs forward, its hind quarters turning slowly in the mud. Then suddenly the downward pull gave way, and with a final effort the animal managed to free itself, rolling over towards the firmer ground before getting to its feet. Stumbling along, it made its way to the trees, where it was greeted by the chatter of squirrels and where the woodfern had covered the earth with a thick light-green carpet. Covered in sweat the animal let its head hang down, trembling and shaking. The calf left the tarn after that dreadful experience, but the old cows continued to enjoy their mud baths all through the summer.

Dragon-flies seemed to like the tarn as well, these long, shining, blue fairy-like creatures. The " troll " dragon-fly was the most common and gave the tarn its name. The first ones appeared in the middle of June, darting about quickly, but they did not really start hatching until midsummer, carefully choosing a warm sunny day and some warm calm water. After a while the larvae would get restless and leave the bottom of the tarn, where they had been waiting and creeping around, frightening all other living things with their menacing double bent lower jaw. Filling their bowels with water, then emptying them again, they would propel themselves forward, using their clumsy tails to steer until they reached the surface. Finally they climbed a sprig of maidenhair or a reed, rising in tens of thousands, their shiny armour glittering in the sunlight.

But the ants were lying in wait, and size and strength were of no avail against the ants, as they were outnumbered and the ants were very bold. But many larvae succeeded in finding a reed, clung to it

The Common Aeshna. By mid-summer the larvae are ready to hatch. During the daytime they creep up a reed, looking terrifying and ugly. The warm sun dries up the hard outer shell, which cracks and splits after an hour or so.

Page 130, and page 131 (top half).

The Common Aeshna. The fly's body shoots out and bends backwards, still cramped up, the head and body then swell and the legs stiffen. Half way out the dragon-fly throws itself forwards, catching hold of the shell and pulling itself right out. Its wings resemble creased silk rags, but soon they open and dry, turning light green and becoming translucent. This dragon-fly grows to be one of the most beautiful insects in the wood, ready for a summer of hunting flies and midges.

Leucorrhinia dubia (Lind.), *the white-faced dragon-fly.*

tightly and climbed up jerkily, stopping half way to let the sun dry them. After an hour or two their tails would start beating forwards and backwards, bending up and down, they would then hunch their backs up until their armour split, and hundreds of dragon-flies were hatched to the sound of cracking echoing across the tarn.

The hunched backs sharpened, then new heads and legs pushed their way out, followed by light yellowish green clammy bodies. The large feelers were wet and shrivelled, still quite insensitive. Bending backwards the body swelled, the eyes cleared and became brighter, legs were drawn in and slowly things sorted themselves out. The clammy bodies dried and hardened, gaining colour and turning green and yellow with a touch of brown. Slowly the hind quarters glided forwards, wings became free, looking like creased wet silk rags. The legs were stretched and felt around for something to hold on to. When most of the dragon-fly had crawled out of its shell, it curled up, then—feeling its way forwards—crept out of the case, and let it fall to the ground.

In a few hours the colourless silk rags which were to become wings swelled and were spread out, turning a matt yellow shade with net-like veins. The body darkened, the eyes turned large and black, the yellow tint in the wings disappeared and then cleared quickly, becoming transparent and shimmering, spread out horizontally, quivering the whole time.

The dragon-flies started waving their wings as though testing them for flight, flapping them quickly and eagerly, the wing beats getting quicker and more intensive. Rising slowly they made their way through the grass until they were free, rising vertically towards the sun and the warmth, heading for a summer of feasting on flies and midges.

The tarn was transformed. Dragon-flies in their hundreds rose from the grass and reeds, all attracted towards the sun. The air seemed to glisten and quiver with pulsating life. Some of the newly hatched dragon-flies made their way over to the trees and the clearing, others made for the lake and new hunting grounds, but most of them remained at the tarn, rising and sinking among the surrounding trees, but always returning. They chased one another, resting now and then on maiden-hair or dry twigs, always in search of the sun and the warmth of its rays.

The trout in the tarn knew well enough what was going on. Never had been heard such a plop plopping all over the tarn, never had the surface of the water been so peppered with the ripples of leaping

133

A lizard has crept up on to an old root, bringing her young to enjoy the warmth of the sun, while the tree creeper is busy on a rotted tree trunk.

fish, as they threw themselves right out of the water in their efforts to catch the dragon-flies as they skimmed a few inches above the surface, darting jerkily here and there when they changed direction.

The bog round about was a fine breeding ground for innumerable insects, and the foresters had not yet attempted to drain this part of the forest for new planting, so there was no human interference with their breeding. In this wild world round the tarn nature was allowed free reign. But the insect world had little chance of getting out of hand, for insects have so many enemies. If they are not devoured by larger insects, they are the natural prey of fish, birds and even bats, which in their mad zig-zag flight live by the destruction of countless insects.

A tree creeper had built a nest in a decayed stump where the stream ran into the tarn. Soon its chicks would fly out in search of food. Sitting on a stump a fledgling watched the tarn, fascinated by the rich assortment it had to offer, but not yet daring to go over there. It was still too small and weak, and the dragon-flies could drag it down into the water.

With the sinking sun an evening mist settled over the tarn, shadows lengthened, flies and gadflies had gone, the dragon-flies chased the gnats, catching them in their flight and swallowing them, darting from left and right, rising and sinking.

Enok had been out for an evening stroll, and came along past the tarn. His sack slung over his shoulder, he moved slowly and quietly. As he stopped and looked through the trees, he saw the glittering wings and heard the first chatter of the teals. He stayed a while, fascinated by this teeming, shimmering life. A young fox crept through the damp grass, under twigs and ferns, jumping from time to time, then stopping to cock its ears. A twig cracked and the leaves were parted, revealing a wet black nose, followed by a head; then another, and yet another appeared. Enok imitated their call. Two of the cubs jumped around in the maidenhair, their ears raised, their blue-black necks clearly visible in the moss. The vixen called from the wood behind, frightening the cubs until one of them saw a dragon-fly skimming over the grass.

Crouching down, the young fox watched and prepared to pounce, then it leapt forward, but missed the dragon-fly, which lost its balance and knocked against a reed, its wings buzzing madly, till it was caught by another cub.

Now they all crept forward—all six of them in a line. Crouching down in the grass they watched the dragon-flies eagerly, hopping and

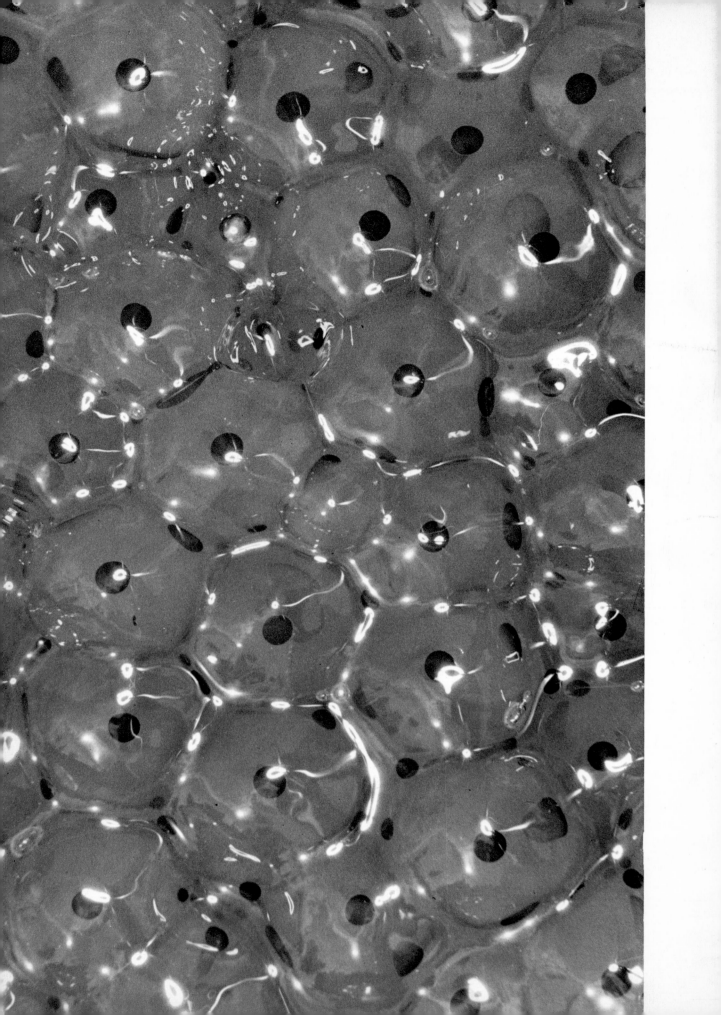

The tarn is popular with all water creatures. The water-boatman flies around, its feet unnaturally magnified in the water. The frog lays its spawn and watches from a short way off, her head wet and shiny, with large protruding eyes and fantastically wide mouth.

darting forwards like dirty yellow flames through the haze of the summer evening. Their barks echoed across the moss and water and out into the darkness of the wood. When two excited cubs collided and rolled over, they started to fight, growling and barking. Another cub rushed after a dragon-fly, jumped and landed in the shallow water. Soaking wet, it climbed out looking very tiny and thin, shook its fur, and licked its lips and found an injured dragon-fly stuck to them.

The game continued. The friendly tone had left the vixen's bark ; now she sounded hoarse and sharp, but her cubs did not hear her, for they were too busy with the joys of dragon-fly hunting. Suddenly the vixen rushed out from under a bush and grabbed one of the cubs by the scruff of its neck and carried it into the wood. Frightened and surprised, the cub squealed. The hunting had come to an end. The cubs went down through the long grass to the wood, only their tracks remained, while the odd dragon-fly continued to dart in and out of the bog cotton.

A fox has a hard life, and well needs its innate cunning if it is to survive in the forest. It has acquired a reputation as a thief and plunderer, and all this is quite true. But it is sometimes hard pressed to find enough food by any means to satisfy itself and its large family— and it does perform a useful service by removing and devouring dead or wounded animals.

As the midsummer night closed in, and after the dragon-flies had gone to rest, bats began to describe their zig-zag and criss-cross flight over the tarn. On the grasses and reeds the empty cases remained, shining in the dew, frightening and ugly as though they were spirits from another world.

From one of the tall oaks an eagle owl called ; *Booo, booo* ! *Booo booo* ! *Booo booo* ! Then, after a moment's silence, it unfolded its wings and glided silently across the waters of the tarn. Just at that moment the moon rose above the trees, spreading a sudden silvery magic over the world, and sending a million flickering ripples across the tarn. This was what the owl was waiting for—now it would be easier to see the thousands of mice which would be emerging from their subterranean homes to play amongst the leaves and grasses. On it swept over the tarn and into the trees, its huge orange eyes glowing in the moonlight.

The tarn and the encircling forest were still alive. The battle for survival continued, and sudden death still awaited the unwary. But the joy and light and colour of the day had passed, and there remained the rather eerie beauty of an ethereal night.

138

Guardian of the stream

Near the waterfall, where the stream winds its way between the spruces and moss covered stones, the dipper had its nest, well concealed under an overhanging rock. Rather like a ski, the rock was wide and flat, and higher upstream there was a pool where shoals of minnows liked to swim, weaving in and out like dark shadows. From the pool the water flowed out over the edge of the rock in a thin wide sheet ; during dry spells it was reduced to a transparent veil, whereas in the spring when the thaw and constant rain filled the stream, the water hung over the edge of the rock like a thick heavy blanket, sometimes causing the rock to tremble under its weight.

Dippers are lively little creatures. They are not gregarious, but live alone or in pairs on the same stretch of water from one year's end till the next. They are fascinating birds to watch, bobbing and curtseying up and down on a boulder in mid-stream, flying swiftly in straight lines, low over the water, diving into the water from a rock, or walking into the water from the shingle at the edge. They seem to be able to remain under the water for a remarkably long time.

Undisturbed by the size of the waterfall, the dipper plunged right through, piercing a small hole in it, and drawn downwards a little by the force of the water. As the bird hit the water it pulled its wings in and bored its way through the sheet of water, rather like a bullet. No other bird could dive like that. Behind the curtain of water, close to the protruding rock, the dipper had woven a nest of fresh green maiden-hair. As large as the head of a toadstool, the nest was wet on the outside from the constant spray. A narrow tunnel led through to the white eggs, gleaming on a bed of dry aspen leaves. The dipper hen was hatching her eggs.

One day a mink made its way to the waterfall. Perhaps it saw the dipper disappearing through the sheet of water, and it may have been prompted by curiosity to inspect further. At all events it found the nest, and grabbed the hen. It dragged the bird down into the water, through the waterfall and out among the stones on the bank. But there on the bank it went straight into one of Enok's old forgotten mink traps. In the autumn when Enok inspected his traps, he found the dead mink in the trap lying on a bed of black and whitish grey feathers.

140

By the following spring the dipper had found a new hen that darted to and fro with him through the sheet of water. Below the waterfall, downstream towards the swamp, was the dipper's favourite fishing ground. There it liked to dart around, knowing every stone and every pebble on the bed of the stream. Sometimes, usually in early spring, other dippers saw the rushing waterfall and came to inspect it, but were greeted with pecking and shrieking and beating wings until they were driven away, leaving the rightful owners each sitting on a stone facing each other, nodding their heads and letting their tails bob up and down, while they uttered a cheerful babble of song. Diving into the water they plunged into the whirling foam, swimming with their wings pointing downwards; bobbing around they braced themselves against the current, eating grubs and small water insects.

Holding a snail in its beak the cock flew up to a nearby stone, shaking the water off its feathers. Legs apart, its white breast showing clearly, it started knocking the snail against the stone in quick hard taps, two or three times in quick succession. As the shell cracked, the bird pulled the snail out, chewed it a few times and swallowed it, then, looking around, babbled to itself. Now that it was satisfied and sleepy, it crept down between two protruding roots only a stone's throw from the waterfall. Sitting there, crouching well down, it could watch its fishing water but remain unseen.

The dipper and the tree creeper that was building in the dry stump close by were good friends, and they were also good neighbours with the capercailzie hen that lived under the fallen tree, as well as the inquisitive young jays. But if a sparrow hawk glided down between the trees, the dipper lay quite still looking like a stone or a root. If a fox should chance to prowl along the banks of the stream, the dipper would fly off downstream, chattering the whole time, going first to a crack in the rock, then to a heap of stones down by the swamp. Having lured the fox away the dipper would leave the intruder and make a wide detour out over the swamp before returning to the waterfall.

Perhaps the dipper's greatest joy was to plunge deliberately into the swift-flowing boulder-strewn torrent—particularly when the stream was in spate, and a mass of mud-coloured foam came hurtling down from the hills, carrying with it leaves, broken branches, and a variety of other debris. How did it manage to stay so long on the river bed? Did it actually walk along the bottom, or did it swim? It is known that dippers can both walk and swim under water, but it is

always amazing to watch the tiny bird disappear into a mass of flowing water, and then reappear a considerable time later—sometimes a surprising distance away.

One evening in early July the dipper fledglings came out to one of the stones below the protecting waterfall—their breasts an oily white, their chirping scarcely audible above the sound of the water. Attracted by the trout in the stream, a mink passed by. It was a lone animal, looking well nourished and with a shiny glossy coat. Moving quickly the mink crept between the stones down to the water, then swam over to the opposite bank, raised its head and looked around before shaking itself.

142

As soon as the dipper saw the mink it rose vertically, then flew hastily up and down the bank, chirping and chattering excitedly before flying to the hen and young to warn them of the danger. The chicks disappeared among the brown-black stones, and the hen joined her mate in his efforts to distract the mink. Chirping and flying to and fro they exerted themselves in desperate efforts.

Suddenly, the hen threw herself into the water near the bank, only a few yards from the mink, spreading her wings in the water. Floundering helplessly, she squeaked and let herself be swept downstream by the current, away from her young. The mink stiffened and hurried after, nearer and nearer, taking cover behind stones and roots, tensing its claws and muscles. Just as the mink was about to pounce, the dipper reached a stone, hopped up on to it and flew up. Then she threw herself into the water again, splashing and chirping and continued to lure the mink farther away towards the swamp, while the cock flew above, rasping and beating his wings.

Much farther downstream the mink dived into a pool of dark water and then forgot all about the dippers, as it slid up on to a stone holding a fish tightly between its forepaws. After slitting the fish it ate it, half closing its eyes to enjoy it to the full. The dippers left, making a wide sweep out over the swamp before returning to the waterfall and their young.

The evening sun still had a great deal of warmth in it as the pair of dippers dived through the waterfall to their waiting family. There was not a breath of wind, and the rushing and bubbling of the water was the only sound to be heard for a time. As the sun sank, insect life became more prevalent over the stream, and the first calls of the owls could be heard.

A pair of wrens came out from their hideout in the bank, and in a jubilee of flutterings and dartings to and fro succeeded in devouring a large number of insects—midges, caddis flies, and caterpillars.

From the nearby lake a chattering of various waterfowl could be heard, and an occasional flapping, splashing, and flight of wings. The heat of the day had passed, and the forest had once again entered that delightful stage which is neither day nor night.

Dew fell with the raw night air, and the scent of the bog myrtle was strong. The night violet turned yellow, cloudberry flowers closed, and from the reeds on the bank of the lake echoed the sound of the pike. The goldeneyes clucked, the diver called, and from the top of the spruce the robin trilled its melancholy song.

143

The lizard enjoys the sun, well camouflaged, while an inquisitive squirrel peeps down from a tree.

Under the bilberries young grouse stumble around, vaguely aware of life's dangers.

The first flocks of mallards are ready to fly. After a morning meal they have crept up among the tussocks on the shore, where they can rest, reflected in the water.

The hazel hen has settled for the night, while the hare leaves its lair to graze on the soft juicy grass, looking and wondering but not frightened.

It is time for the young marten to creep out of its hiding place in the old tree, and to start learning to climb. Weak in the legs it swings and sways alarmingly, but practice makes perfect, and within six months it will be the most agile of the climbing animals in the wood.

Wild minks' island

An old fishing hut lay concealed among the pines at the edge of a bay on the wild minks' island. It was a wooden cabin with the date 1662 carved on the doorpost. There were two bunks, and a hole in the roof for smoke. Outside the hut, heather and bilberry and juniper bushes formed a thick carpet, and among the twigs the remains of an oven and other ancient cooking utensils were to be found. The shore of the island was stony, the wood dense and high, with occasional silver firs rising higher than the other trees.

Now and again Enok crossed over to the old hut, mainly during the summer. As soon as the ice melted and pike started rising, he cast his nets in the few grassy patches along the shore ; in the summer heat, when the perch started hunting, he would wait at the deep pool with his rod, sitting motionless for hours on end ; later on, in the long dark cold November evenings, he would row to and fro over the stormswept water seeing the white bellies of the fish turning in play. Should he leave his catch in the boat while he went into the hut to make his coffee, it would disappear quickly and silently. But should he take it with him inside the hut, a number of small brownish-black heads with wrinkled noses and shiny black eyes would appear in the doorway. It would be the wild mink and its young—four or five of them, sometimes even more.

In the evening light it was not always easy to tell which were the young and which the parent minks, for the young ones were exceedingly fluffy and looked bigger than they were, while the female was in any case much smaller than the male animal. Their fur was wonderfully lustrous, and when the full moon shone over the lake, Enok could see the gleam on the minks' fur as they peered through the doorway of the old hut.

They seldom stayed at the door when Enok looked round, but went scampering away back to the water, where he could hear the splashing as they submerged. For minks are perfectly at home in the water, and can swim below the surface for long periods without coming up for air. They live on fish, frogs, musk-rats, and small birds if they can catch them.

There were always several families of minks living on the island, in burrows near the edge of the water.

Every year there were two or three litters of young mink near the

153

The black-throated diver's legs lie well back, making it awkward for it to walk. When climbing into its nest it pushes and drags itself forward, then—turning its eggs—it sinks down on them. But should the warmth of the sun become too oppressive it will creep back into the water.

After four weeks the young peck their way out. Sometimes the hen will lie heavily on the eggs to crack them, and help the chicks to come out.

The chicks stay in the nest until they are quite dry, but this does not take long, and in next to no time they dart down to the water. If the ground is sloping too much they may roll over a few times and remain flat on their backs, till the hen comes to their rescue.

hut. By midsummer they were half grown. Sitting in a row on the smooth stones along the shore, or standing on their hind legs, they welcomed Enok with short quick yelps before joining in the hunt for fish. From then on until the first frost the mink were everywhere, darting between the stones on the shore, catching small unsuspecting fish, robbing the chaffinch's hidden nest, hissing and spitting at any approaching herring gull. Sometimes they swam over to the osprey's island and sniffed around under their nesting tree ; sometimes a half eaten pike could be found out there.

The female osprey kept a careful eye on them, stretching her neck out over the edge of the nest so that she could hear their movements in the heather, but on the whole she was not bothered by them. Perhaps they were frightened off by her mate, who usually sat and rested on an outstretched branch in the top of a nearby pine, when he was not catching fish for his ravenous brood.

Should there be any mink on the island he watched their movements with keen interest, crouching down, his head drawn in. If the mink started fighting over a half-eaten fish, he would send out a warning signal and the mink would forget their differences and turn towards the osprey, hissing, and guarding their fish savagely. Sometimes a pied wagtail flew over the osprey's nest and dived down at the four-footed invaders, its frightened chatter echoing far out over the lake.

One summer's day a young mink swam out to the boulder on which the gull had made its nest. The two day-old chicks were jumping about on the boulder, soft grey speckled balls of fluff. Spying the young chicks the mink crouched down behind a protruding corner of the boulder, hidden from the gulls. Stretching its claws, its eyes burning, the mink was just about to leap forward when it received a violent blow from a pair of gull's wings. Thrown off the stone, it fell with a loud splash into the water. That was the first and last time the mink climbed up to the gull's nest.

Mink are brave and inquisitive creatures and they are interested not only in gulls. The goosander sometimes found it difficult to warn its young out on the stones, and the only grouse that decided to nest on the island was caught and eaten before her eggs were hatched. But sometimes the mink were too brave.

There was a narrow sound between the long narrow osprey island and the long peninsular from the mainland. The banks sloped down, covered with high grass between the stones, with a narrow belt of reeds beyond. Down there, quite near the water, the black-throated diver had built its nest of dry and withered maidenhair.

What a beautiful bird she was, with her fine black and white stripes on the sides of her neck and breast. Her thin grey head was armed with a long slender black bill, which was razor sharp at the point and could be a most valuable weapon of defence against prowling animals.

One morning in June the hen was hatching her large brown speckled eggs and the lake shimmered in the sun. Flies were buzzing around, and high up above the lake a buzzard circled, scattering all the small fish. Darting to and fro a dragon-fly was searching for food. In the narrow sound the knotted beech trees were reflected in the water. With her beak half open the black-throated diver breathed heavily, her eyes blinked slowly, gradually closed completely and her head sank down. Suddenly she awoke, raised her head and opened her eyes, looking around sleepily. Soon she started blinking again and nodded off to sleep, her head sinking farther and farther down as it seemed to get heavier and heavier.

After a few hours' sleep in the heat of the sun she heard a rustle. She awoke quickly, shaking her head a few times and closing her beak. Wide awake now, she saw two small shining eyes in the yellow grass. The mink disappeared, but reappeared quickly at the edge of a stone under a willow bush down between the reeds. Nearer and nearer it crept, more and more bravely, whiskers tense. Drawing her head back, the diver pressed herself down into the nest, making herself small and flat, but her eyes were wide and keen.

The mink crept nearer and nearer, stepping back nervously now and then, moving forward again, looking around cautiously. The diver remained quite still, only her eyes moved. Step by step the mink approached, creeping in from the side through the thickest sedge, quivering and frightened. Gliding through the grass, it was only about a foot away from the nest when the diver suddenly thrust her beak out, quick as lightning. Her neck was long and thin and her whole body seemed to follow into the sedge. The mink fled squealing into the reeds, bearing a wound that would show its scar for a long time.

The black-throated diver settled down again in her nest. Raising herself on her tail she turned her eggs slowly and methodically, then sank down again. Shaking her tail feathers she changed her position and kicked with her legs, but was not comfortable. Standing up again, she moved the eggs together, and seemed quite happy as she settled down for the second time.

The sun shone, flies hummed, and soon the diver was panting

160

Young gulls are bold little fellows, running over uneven stones with remarkable self-assurance.

again, her beak half open, her eyes slowly closing up, forming small slits as she dozed off again.

A huge dragon-fly flew by, its wings covered with a network of veins, shimmering and flashing in the sunlight. A long procession of ants wound its way slowly through the pebbles and boulders in front of the diver. A butterfly hovered gaily above the lake, and a flock of goldfinches whirred overhead. A multitude of mosquitoes hummed monotonously in the undergrowth. High summer reigned over the lake.

The sun tempts out all the animals and flowers. The slowworm peers out, while a large butterfly clings to a mossy stone, and the night violet opens out its white scented flowers.

Drama down at the old root

The redwings in the owl's wood breed late. As late as the end of May or early June their song is still high and full, their whistle echoing round the wood in the early morning and in the evenings ; later it takes on a more melancholy note, turning into more of a chatter than a whistle. When the redwing in the wood stops singing, another up by the lake answers, and a third out on the swamp joins in ; then the first bird starts up again, call answering call. Their high piping and chattering is lost among the trees. Sometimes one of the redwings changes the tune, introducing its own ambitious composition, till the others take it up, repeating it for hours on end, night after night, until another new tune is composed to drown the first.

There must have been a great many redwings in this part of the forest, their thin fluting could be heard in its endless variations by the lake, on the edge of the tarn, out on the bog, and around the rubbish dump outside Enok's cottage. They were fine looking birds with their boldly speckled breasts and conspicuous stripes through the eyes, and added a distinctive touch of music and colour to the forest.

Even the biting cold of midwinter did not seem to keep them under cover, and when the forest lay under its heavy blanket of snow these little birds were to be seen in quite numerous flocks roaming the countryside, and covering surprising distances. But in this fine warm summer weather their thoughts had long been turned to the rearing of young, and they were no longer gregarious, but dotted about the forest in old tree stumps, bushes, and thickets.

Not far from the tarn a fir had been blown over by the autumn storms, the roots torn up with a large cake of earth clinging to them. Loose roots were left hanging down, raspberry canes and sprigs of bilberry swaying in the wind. Here, below this root, the redwings had chosen to build their nest, walled in by earth, stones, and twisted roots.

From early June the hen hatched her eggs down in the root, while her mate sang down to her from a nearby pine. At midsummer the chicks cracked their eggs, and that week the redwing stopped singing, becoming uneasy and nervous. Whenever a weasel or jay appeared, he would start fluttering around, pecking wildly ; or when the elk passed with its heavy plod, he would return excitedly to his nest. The two parent birds would chatter away to each other to distract any intruders, but if they were left undisturbed they would

feed their young all day long with grubs and insects, resting for a while in the middle of the day as the sun beat down on the dry soil and the chicks lay gasping, their beaks wide open.

Gradually the chicks' down turned into feathers, stomachs swelled and they became more and more cramped inside the nest. They pushed and kicked one another until the smallest chick was driven up to the edge of the nest, where he sat quiet and frightened, struggling desperately to get food. But the other chicks always took the food that was brought to the nest, and it was pushed out of the way.

Not far from the redwings' root there was another old root, grey with wind and age, split by rain and sun, knotted and twisted. There was a round black hole in it, an odd whim of nature. This was where the weasel lived—a small weasel, the fiercest and most hungry of all the weasels, but also the most beautiful and quickest. It had made a lair deep down in the root, a sort of nest where it had given birth to six young. By now the young weasels were as big as shrews, only much thinner and longer. One or two tiny heads peeped out of the hole, others darted in and out of the surrounding brushwood, disappearing immediately a buzzard appeared overhead, but popping up again just as quickly when the robin's song blended with the humming of the flies, or when the cry of a jay caught by a hawk echoed through the wood. Frollicking in joyful play they chased one another up and down the root, bit each other's fur and ran down into the brushwood, spitting and grinding their teeth at each other so that they became frightened and returned to the nest.

When their mother returned with a warm vole hanging from her jaws, they all rushed down to meet her. Throwing themselves at the vole they tore at it, squabbling and fighting until the metallic warning cry of the pied flycatcher cut the air. But by then the vole had gone, all but the tail, which swayed on a bilberry twig, and slipped down into the brushwood where it was hidden from view and would not be found until it was eaten by ants.

By midsummer there were no small rodents left near the root, and the weasel had to go farther afield. Her young had grown and were hungrier and rougher in their play, and it became more and more difficult to find food. A late hazel chick would have to do, even though it was heavy to drag back to the nest.

One evening the weasel was sitting in the brushwood near the redwings' nest, listening and watching. Wrinkling up her nose she

166

sniffed. The sun spread its golden veil on the pine roots, midges rose and dived in a cloud, and the redwing's melancholy trill echoed from the tarn. Then the redwing came over carrying food in its beak, landed on the bare root and hopped into the nest, pushing his head into one of the gaping mouths, cleaned the nest a little and then went off among the trees. The weasel saw everything.

Quivering and trembling with excitement she lifted one paw, eyes gleaming. As the chicks sank back into the nest so that only their beaks could be seen over the edge, the weasel crept through the brushwood towards them. Taking cover in raspberry and bilberry leaves she made her way forward, tapping an irritating bee with her paw on the way, and frightening a lizard.

She stopped and listened, looking up at the nest, then jumped forward quickly. Reaching the nest, she stopped again and listened, then lent over quickly and put her teeth into the neck of the nearest chick and bit hard. Pitiful cries broke the silence ; two small wings beat helplessly, then both the weasel and the chick tumbled down the slope in a whirl of down, legs and fur. The dry soil flew around them and the small stones clattered.

Then the chattering started. Two voices from different directions came in and met at the tree. Beating around in the bilberry twigs the hen chattered and chirped frantically. The weasel made off, pulling her catch through the brushwood. It got caught in a twig, was freed, and then got caught again. The young weasels heard the redwings' chatter and the woodlark's fine warning cry, the willow tit's harsh call and the bullfinch's short alarm cry. They understood—they knew that food was coming, and went out into the brushwood to enjoy their feast under the budding bilberries.

The following night the weasel repeated her visit to the redwings' root, again when the parents were away. New cries echoed out, followed by the beating of wings. The young weasels went out to meet their mother again, and this time they seemed larger and more experienced.

In the end there was only one chick left in the redwings' nest ; it was the smallest one that had always been downtrodden by the others. It was much larger now. During the past twenty-four hours it had had five times its normal ration of food, and had grown brave and strong.

This evening, after the sun had set and a few peals of thunder had shaken down some refreshing rain, the young weasels felt experienced. As the mother made her way to the nest, she was followed by a long winding line of young weasels, all of them hungry.

The fifth and last young redwing was always hungry, making up for its previous starvation and the rough treatment it had received from its brothers. Lying at the edge of the nest it gasped for more food, alone and quite spoilt. Following her usual route up to the nest the weasel leant forward, almost idly. Suddenly there was a loud crescendo of noise like a wave or a rising wind and the young redwing flew out. It sank down into the bushes and raspberry leaves, untouched and unseen.

Sitting up at the edge of the nest the weasel looked around amazed, neck outstretched, ears cocked. As she slid down the earthy root she was greeted by six pairs of frightened, hungry eyes, filled with bewilderment.

By now, however, the young weasels were no longer the slim tiny bits of life they had been when the first redwing chick had been carried to their hole, and they were beyond their mother's power to support any longer. Soon they would have to go off and make their own way in this dangerous world, where enemies lurked in every tree, and even the blue vault of the open sky was a constant danger, for at any moment death could plummet from the skies with awful speed, and without warning.

But a weasel had less cause to be afraid than many of the creatures of the forest, for the weasel is a born hunter, and is a source of constant fear to a great many of the other animals and birds—some of them bigger than itself. It is so tiny that it can pursue its prey through very small holes and crevices in rocks, or into long winding burrows underground.

It is also a highly competent climber, and can follow its victims up the trunks and along the branches of trees, although it is more frequently to be found on the ground. Water presents no obstacle to it, for it is an able swimmer, and ducklings and other young waterfowl can never be entirely safe when there are weasels around. Its victims, indeed, include a great many of the smaller denizens of the forest— rats, mice, voles, moles, water-rats, frogs, lizards, and small birds— and, of course, the young of many larger birds.

For its diminutive size the weasel is an incredibly bloodthirsty animal, and is possessed of remarkable courage. The female will defend her young with desperation against any attacker, and will sacrifice her own life if necessary rather than desert them.

169

The changeling

During our sojourn in the forest we have seen a good deal of the apparent cruelty of nature—nature red in tooth and claw, where almost every creature pursues some other creature, and is in its turn pursued. When we are first confronted with this eternal battle for survival, this ceaseless hunt, this bloody battlefield in the wilds—the air frought with terror and the meaning of mercy totally unknown— we tend to attempt to apply moral judgment, forgetting that where there is no reason there can be no morals either. Where all life must literally fight for survival, only the law of the jungle can apply, and where all life is governed by instinct there can be no question of right or wrong. Only brute strength or cunning is right, and the lack of these is inevitably and mercilessly wrong.

This is more than obvious, but it is nevertheless hard for us humans to give up our innate habit of applying moral judgment.

There is at least one instance in nature, however, where human reason and morals are at variance, and where human judgment has taken different sides. Is the cuckoo brilliantly clever, arranging for all the hard labour of house building and bringing up a family to be done free of charge by other birds—without these birds even realising that they have undertaken this task, to the detriment and death of their own rightful family ? Or is it the meanest and most despicable creature that lives in the forest ?

Long before midsummer a wren had built her round nest among the lower branches of a pine. While she was laying, a new egg suddenly appeared in the nest when she was out. It was the same colour as the other eggs, only much longer and thicker. The wren looked at it, nodded and twittered, laid another egg, and then started to hatch them.

Time passed. Her mate continued building the half finished nest, singing now and then with a metallic note in his trill. By midsummer the eggs were hatched. Out of the large egg a big blind chick emerged,

It is no sinecure to be foster-mother to a young cuckoo, especially for the tiny wren. Sometimes she is almost afraid, the appetite seems so voracious, and the mouth so immense that she almost disappears into it.

No matter how much she feeds it, its beak is always open demanding more. Then she grows tired and angry, and becomes so excited that she bobs up and down, beating her wings.

naked and exceedingly ugly. Its wide stomach seemed swollen, its eyelids enormous and its mouth unusually wide.

Right from the start the big chick was restless, pushing and shoving the other chicks, trying to get all the food. In two days it had grown strong and cheeky, and it pushed the other chicks out of the small entrance to the nest, pecking and pressing them on to their backs, and shoving them out one after the other. They lay dead on the ground below until they were eaten by ants.

The big chick continued to grow, filling the nest until it split the walls. It swelled up but not quite so quickly as before. Its wings developed and its tail grew more and more pointed every day. It seemed to require feeding every other minute. By the end of July the chick had difficulty in lying down, and the nest seemed to have turned into a hollow platform under its stomach. It was lazy and stupid, blinked sleepily all the time, and hardly paid any attention to its fostermother's chatter and offers of food. But it ate everything that was brought—a grub, a butterfly, a fly—then ruffled its feathers and looked pleased with itself. Then it stretched its legs and went to sleep again.

One day the rest of the nest collapsed and the chick hopped over to an old bleached root and to freedom. Now it became more lively and alert. Looking around, it stretched and explored the area down in the wood. By evening it grew sleepy and crouched down, ruffled itself up and dozed off, only to be awakened by the wren's call and promise of more food. The wren came down, slowly at first, then creeping through the brushwood, bringing a fly in her beak. She flew round the chick a few times, bobbing and chattering incessantly, then went over to a nearby twig and stretched herself to her full height, thrusting her head down the chick's orange-red throat. The young bird took the food without noticing it, without even having to swallow. The fly was put so far down its throat that it went down on its own, while the chick continued to gape hungrily.

Sitting on the twig the wren bobbed up and down, then she hopped down into the brushwood, chattering as she looked for more insects, darting here and there like quicksilver. Busily she hopped around an old ant hill, looked under a root and she caught a passing butterfly, her stumpy tail pointing up at right angles, shining with a reddish glow in the evening sun.

As the sun went down the wren became tired and the chick grew impatient, turning restlessly and snapping at the air. The wren hurried

174

dutifully along, carrying a little green bug in her beak. She seemed eager and yet frightened and went straight to the chick, clawed herself into its ruffled neck feathers and held fast, beating her wings and nearly disappearing into the gaping beak. Her grip on the feathers was weak and she slid down on to the root beside the chick, which still kept its beak wide open, towering over its fostermother, immense and over-whelming as though intending to eat her.

The wren had had enough. She hopped back to a nearby twig, stretched herself and pushed her head into the open beak, once, twice, three times in quick succession. Circling round twice, she bobbed and nodded her head, beating her wings and chattering as she went. Then she vanished among the darkness of the pines, chattering and calling angrily.

The sun sinks, the air grows damp, and the mist rises. The goldcrest has found its perch for the night, but the bats wake up and clamber out of their hollow tree. So does a beetle.

The badger makes its way along the path, looking for grubs and slugs in the soft soil. Eyes are watching all around, the sharpest of all being those of the eagle owl, glowing like embers in the darkness.

Summer night

For half the year the forest lay buried in snow, held in the all-pervading grip of winter. During the grim half-year, when much life perished and most of the remainder retired into a prolonged sleep, the forest knew little variation in weather conditions. True, snow might be falling or it might merely be lying everywhere, gales might be blowing as if the end of the world was at hand, or the still heavy silence which only deep snow can bring might lie over the forest. But by and large conditions changed little during the winter, and one day and night would be much like another.

The summer, on the other hand, brought infinite variations of weather to the forest. There were days of sparkling, dazzling, shimmering summer heat, when creatures of the forest gasped and panted in the sun. There were days when they cowered under roots or undergrowth, river bank or tuft of grass, while the rain lashed all around in fury, thunder cracked and boomed across the skies, and lightning rent the heavens.

There were long spells of drought when the marsh almost dried up completely, and lake and tarn shrank drastically leaving many water creatures stranded, and the stream dwindled to a mere trickle, revealing the dipper's hide-out under the waterfall, and leaving fish floundering in shallow pools which had become temporarily stagnant.

There was a time when rain had fallen solidly for days on end over the forest, turning the ditches into large streams, and the streams into raging torrents. The marsh had turned into a lake overnight, and from the hills to the north water came seeping, racing, roaring—carrying with it the corpses of hapless animals who had been washed from their homes, swirling over nests and burrows, wiping out a colony of ants in a few brief seconds, hurling aside huge piles of brushwood that had contained countless tiny homes.

The death toll had been appalling. Even the water creatures had suffered in the chaos, and countless animals, birds, and insects had perished. Not even the nests on high branches had been safe, for many had been hurled to the ground by the sheer weight of falling water, and had shared in the common disaster.

Fortunately such flooding is not frequent in the forest, but when it happens during the height of the nesting and breeding season it

takes nature some little time to put right the balance which had been so violently upset by the catastrophe.

High summer arrived in the forest, life buzzed and hummed contentedly, and as time passed it seemed as if these long days and short nights had become a permanent feature. But almost imperceptibly the long days shortened and the hours of darkness lengthened, the waxy freshness passed off the green leaves of the trees and they took on a dull time-worn appearance. The tall grasses burst into seed, and the first tiny chestnuts began to swell on the chestnut trees. The fledglings had long since left their nests, with the exception of some of the owlets, who always had to be tempted out into the great big world by the parent birds. The young of nearly all the creatures had ventured forth on their own, to face the adventure and the dangers, the hardships and the excitement of life in the forest.

As July passed the days became dry and heavy, filled with sunlight and warm winds, lulled by the rustle of leaves and the lapping of waves, with fleecy white clouds floating majestically overhead. The evening mist rose from thicket and stream, thin and blue, coolly scented and wet with dew. A dragon-fly circled the reeds at the tarn for the last time. The dipper caught its last fish down at the stream. The surviving redwing chick ate its last caterpillar for the day. Having found its perch for the night, the wren cleaned itself for rest. Blinking sleepily from its dry branch, the osprey crouched down. The young woodpeckers stopped calling, leaving their gaping holes dark and empty, and under the heather on the slope the woodcock went out in search of an evening snack of bilberries. Overhead a host of twinkling stars looked down on a silent world.

Slowly the sun sank below the trees, the dusk gathered, and a perfect summer evening passed into night.

Gradually the night animals came to life. The hare made its way softly down to the edge of the swamp, casting a fleeting shadow as it went. Moths flew in the increasing deep blue of the night, and out on the clearing the white rumps of the deer could be seen clearly.

There was plenty of life down at the owl's dry tree stump. The larger owlets had pushed their way to the opening, trampling on one another, pushing and beating with their wings. Now and then they would lean out, their reddish-yellow eyes gleaming. The mother owl flew around in the surrounding trees, luring and tempting them out, holding a newly caught mouse in one claw. One of the owlets was pushed from behind and nearly fell out ; with a sharp shrill cry it gave the others a dig with its half-open beak. When the badger

The young owl is quite ravenous. Taking the mouse by the head it tries to swallow—no easy task for a youngster.

It manages slowly, and after a little while only the bulging hind quarters of the mouse stick out.

The mouse has gone, the owl round and content.

passed, digging in the moss, cutting the roots as it went and flinging soil up all around, they remained quiet and watched wide-eyed. When the badger sat on its haunches, scratching itself behind its ears, its claws going through the fur like a grater, the young owlets leaned right back, one of them falling back into the hollow of the nest. Peace was restored in the wood.

But not complete peace.

Bats lived down in a hollow stump near the tarn, and their day's rest had just come to an end. They hung upside down and looked around, hungry and rested. One of them combed its fur with a hind leg, while another cleaned itself with its mouth ; others licked their wings. They started arguing, pushing and biting, squeaking with their mouths wide open and showing rows of tiny sharp teeth. One bat turned over completely and climbed up the inside wall of the hollow tree, clawing and biting its way up. Reaching the edge of the hole, it climbed out on to a protruding twig, screwed up its eyes at the light of the night sky and yawned—its white teeth shining. A shadow passed over the hollow tree as the bat took to the air and circled around, swiftly and silently.

Turning in its flight an owl made for the black tarn. A clutch of frightened goosanders piped and squeaked as it passed, the chicks hurrying out on to dry land, beating their tiny wings against the water. The owl flew on and alighted on a pine tree. Listening to the plod of the elk, it sharpened its gaze on the sandpiper which was busy on a high stone near the water, and made a swift plunge to catch a long-tailed mouse close to the tarn. It did not tempt its young to come out, but went straight to the nest. The mother owl met it there, flapping angrily and chasing it from tree to tree, pecking and beating it.

Holding the mouse in her claws, the mother called and tempted her young, holding the mouse in her beak as she moved from tree to tree. The two largest owlets pushed their way up into the hole ; they were hungry and their gaze was fixed on the hanging mouse. One of them bobbed up and down, leaning farther and farther out until it jumped, beating its tiny wings. Turning and squawking it flew over to the young pine, became entangled in the twigs, and finally alighted on a branch. Looking and feeling remarkably small it sat there and gazed at this strange world, before moving over to a nearby stump.

The mother owl was excited and rolled her eyes, and went down to her owlet and gave it the mouse whole. It took the mouse, turned it over, knocked it over the head, opened its beak and tried to swallow it. Slowly the mouse began to disappear and the owlet had to have a

rest.   The mouse swelled as it was pressed together, and the skin became tight, tail and hind legs sticking out in opposite directions.

The young owl had to start again.   Eyes rolling and spluttering away it finally succeeded, and slowly the mouse's hindquarters disappeared.   The owlet managed to close its beak with some difficulty, and only one leg and the tail stuck out.   When these last remnants had gone and it could shut its beak completely, it closed its eyes, puffed itself out and dozed off—dead to the world.

Meantime another young owl had left the security of the nest, and was sitting on a branch trying to swallow another mouse, having the same difficulties, but succeeding in the end.

Dew fell and the moon rose.   A cluster of silver birches drooped their ethereal branches gracefully on the sky-line, and a fantastically gnarled oak showed its knotted and twisted branches, silhouetted against the soft silvery disc of the moon.   A passing fox jumped nervously as a frog leapt from under its nose, and paused—paw in the air—to survey the wonderful magic of the night.

Flutterings could be heard in the branches, and rustlings amongst the grasses and pine needles below.   A silent shadow floated by as an owl swept noiselessly overhead.   From the nearby lake came the sounds of the waterfowl, while the gurgle and chatter of the stream carried far on the night air.

Golden maidenhair seeds shone in the moonlight, the water of the tarn glittered and quivered, a young weasel sat on a birch stump waiting for a young mouse which was hiding nervously under the root. The young marten was practising jumping and climbing in the dry pine.   Ducklings chattered in the water, their chatter carrying a remarkably long way in the still night air.

A large frog puffed itself out to a fantastic size until it looked quite frightening, with its shiny mottled skin glittering and its mouth unnaturally wide.

A beetle crept out under a bush, distorted by the night shadows. The scent of the bog-myrtle was strong.   Glow worms shone, and night moths circled round birch and elder ; the yellow eyes of the eagle owl pierced the darkness, searching the brushwood.   Out on the lake the tiny islands were wrapped in mist.

The young owlets could be heard from a long way off.   The last one had just left the nest.   Keeping together they moved from tree to tree, or sat together on a branch, crying and hooting in chorus as the wood was gradually enveloped in the blue mist of the summer night.

190